James Clerk Maxwell
Physicist and Natural Philosopher

DSB EDITIONS

Benjamin Franklin
Scientist and Statesman
I. Bernard Cohen

•

Antoine-Laurent Lavoisier
Chemist and Revolutionary
Henry Guerlac

•

James Clerk Maxwell
Physicist and Natural Philosopher
C.W.F. Everitt

JAMES CLERK MAXWELL

Physicist and Natural Philosopher

C. W. F. Everitt

Adjunct Professor
Hansen Laboratories of Physics
Stanford University

Illustrated with photographs

CHARLES SCRIBNER'S SONS
New York

1 3 5 7 9 11 13 15 17 19   C/C   20 18 16 14 12 10 8 6 4 2
1 3 5 7 9 11 13 15 17 19   C/P   20 18 16 14 12 10 8 6 4 2

Printed in the United States of America
Library of Congress Catalog Card Number 75-7594
ISBN 0-684-14253-6 (cloth)
ISBN 0-684-14253-8 (paper)

In memory of my father,
Robert Arthur Everitt,
who first roused my interest in
the history of science and engineering

Publisher's Note

DSB Editions constitute a series of books developed from articles in the *Dictionary of Scientific Biography*. Each is a biography of a major scientist.

The *Dictionary of Scientific Biography,* published by Charles Scribner's Sons under the sponsorship of the American Council of Learned Societies, was designed to provide reliable information on the history of science through articles on the professional lives of scientists. It covers all periods from classical antiquity to modern times but does not include careers of living persons. In many instances the articles represent either the first or the most important study yet made of an individual's body of work. The authors are professional historians of science or professionals in a particular scientific area who also take a scholarly interest in the past. The aim was to include scientific figures whose contributions made an identifiable difference to knowledge as a whole. Each article concludes with a bibliography that guides the reader to the original scientific works and to biographical sources covering personal and public life. Some articles also contain reference notes.

DSB Editions contain the complete contents of

the original article, plus a preface by the author, a section of illustrations, and an index. The texts have been revised by the authors and in some cases expanded to add further personal data, and the bibliographies have been brought up to date when necessary.

Contents

Preface

The man who was described in 1931 by Sir James Jeans as the greatest mathematical physicist the world had seen since Newton is not as widely known as he should be. Maxwell died young. His inherited social position freed him from one common impulse toward pursuing scientific fame, and his engaging mixture of modesty and arrogance left him content to transform physics without proclaiming the fact to the world at large. Yet lack of recognition is not lack of impact. Anyone who switches on a color television set might reflect that the theory advanced by Maxwell in 1865 led to the discovery of radio waves by Heinrich Hertz two decades later, and that Maxwell himself laid down the principles of color photography and in 1861 projected the first color photograph. For physicists Maxwell has far higher claims.

My own interest in Maxwell began by chance at the age of seventeen through reading the official *Life of James Clerk Maxwell* by Lewis Campbell and William Garnett, a work I should like to commend. Its tone belongs to the 1870s rather than the 1970s and its physics is weak, but the chapters on Maxwell's first twenty-five years have a brilliance of detail and a psychological penetration rare in Victorian or any other biographies. Maxwell was fortunate in having Campbell as his friend. Campbell's later biographical work on Benjamin Jowett, the Greek scholar and Master of Balliol College, Oxford, was equally searching, as Sir Geoffrey Faber's *Jowett* reveals. In an interesting background letter quoted by Faber, Campbell distinguished two styles of biography, one written shortly after the subject's death to capture elusive personal impressions, and another, which he called the *éloge,* "the considered, judicious, well-proportioned, but *short* biography, which cannot be undertaken until a sufficient length of time has passed." The present volume does not fulfill all of Campbell's ideals, but I hope it will serve as a preliminary scientific *éloge* of Maxwell, and encourage some readers to take the broad view of physics that justifies use of the older and prouder name natural philosophy.

Many people have supported my researches. For assistance in locating Maxwelliana and providing background, I am particularly grateful to Brigadier John Wedderburn-Maxwell, who also allowed me to photograph watercolor paintings of scenes from Maxwell's childhood; to the late Miss Dorothy Wedderburn-Maxwell, Miss Frances Dunn, Sam Callendar, James Urquhart, A. E. B. Owen of Cambridge University Library, I. Kaye of the Royal Society, C. R. Dodwell of Trinity College, Cambridge, E. J. Kenney of Peterhouse, Cambridge, and W. P. D. Wightman of the University of Aberdeen and the staffs of other libraries mentioned in the bibliography. Professional colleagues who have given more than ordinary help include Joan Bromberg, Stephen Brush, Christopher Calladine, R. V. Jones, Thomas Kuhn, Derek Price, Thomas Simpson, and my brother Alan Everitt. To all of these and to other helpful friends I express my thanks.

A Portfolio of Pictures

James Clerk Maxwell, about 1870, from a portrait formerly in the possession of Miss F. K. Dunn

18

Watercolors painted about 1841 by Maxwell's first cousin Jemima Wedderburn

(Above) The Boy (Maxwell) with his father (John Clerk Maxwell) and the dog Toby.

(Left, top) "Tubbing on the Duckpond": *(left to right)* The Artist (Jemima Wedderburn), Sam Murdoch, The Boy, The Tutor, Sandy Fraser, Mrs. James Wedderburn (Jemima's mother), John Clerk Maxwell, Toby; three alarmed ducks in the background.

(Left, bottom) "A Ploughing Match": at right, The Artist, John Clerk Maxwell, and The Boy are hastening away from the rain. The judges are standing by the cart.

Maxwell's color top. The top, developed from the one invented in 1849 by Maxwell's teacher J. D. Forbes, has two sets of tinted papers, arranged in adjustable sectors. When the top is spun the colors mix in the eye. The observer adjusts either or both sets of papers until they match. A color equation is then formed in terms of the exposed angles for each color.

(Right) Maxwell at Cambridge in 1855, holding the color top.

20

Glenlair House, the Maxwell family home near Dalbeattie, Kirkcudbright-shire, in southwestern Scotland: *(above)* photograph taken in 1860 of the original house designed and built by Maxwell's father John Clerk Maxwell; *(right)* photograph taken in 1880 of the house as enlarged and improved by Maxwell in 1867.

23

Peter Guthrie Tait, school friend of Maxwell at Edinburgh, afterward Professor of Natural Philosophy at Edinburgh University, co-author with Sir William Thomson of the famous Thomson-Tait *Treatise on Natural Philosophy,* and Maxwell's most active scientific correspondent (photograph taken about 1870).

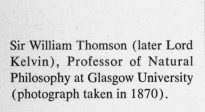

Sir William Thomson (later Lord Kelvin), Professor of Natural Philosophy at Glasgow University (photograph taken in 1870).

Lewis Campbell, Maxwell's friend and biographer, and a well-known classical scholar, as portrayed on the Lewis Campbell medal of St. Andrew's University.

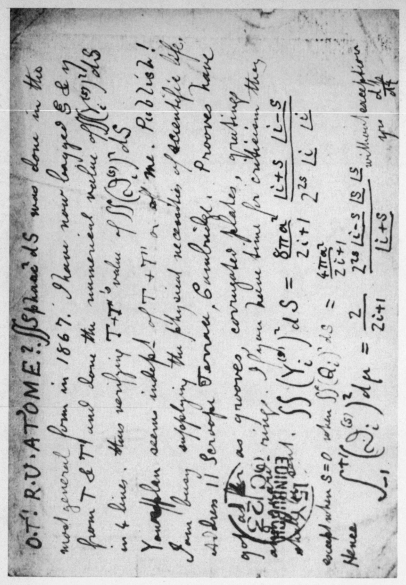

Postcard from Maxwell (dp/dt) to Tait (T'), October 23, 1871. After the British Post Office introduced the halfpenny postcard in 1869 Thomson, Tait, and Maxwell started a regular correspondence. Thomson's name was usually abreviated to T, Tait's to T', and Maxwell was dp/dt in recognition of an equation in Tait's *Sketch of Thermodynamics* which read dp/dt = JCM.

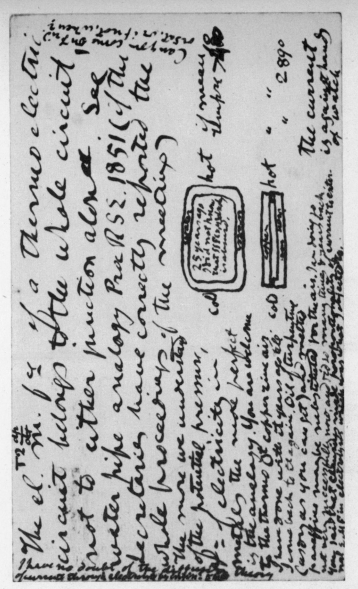

Postcard from Thomson to Maxwell (T2 dp/dt), 1876.

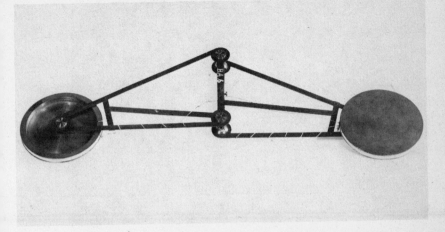

(Above) Balance arm from the apparatus with which Maxwell and Charles Hockin in 1868 measured the ratio of electrostatic to electromagnetic forces; they established that the quantity $\underline{c}$ having dimensions of velocity, which appears in the definitions of the two quantities, is very nearly equal to the velocity of light.

(Left) Maxwell's dynamical top, invented in 1857 to demonstrate motions of a spinning body. The top is supported on a steel point near its center of mass. Under the cover are ten screws used in varying the magnitude and directions of the principal moments and adjusting the mass-center. Maxwell applied the principles of colorimetry to provide an angular readout of the spin-axis by means of a card with four colored quadrants attached to the upper end of the top.

Apparatus used by Maxwell and his wife, Katherine Mary Dewar, between 1864 and 1866, to determine the viscosity of gases as a function of pressure

Maxwell and his wife, photographed in Scotland about 1875.

Maxwell's apparatus for investigating the gyromagnetic action of an electro-magnet, 1861. The effect for which Maxwell was looking was eventually discovered in 1907 by S. J. Barnett.

Apparatus used by Donald MacAlister and Maxwell to verify the inverse square law in electrostatics to 1 part in 10^6. The experiment was a refined version of one performed in 1757 by Henry Cavendish, which remained unknown until Maxwell discovered an account of it in Cavendish's papers.

The Cavendish Laboratory, Cambridge, from the inner court, about 1890. The laboratory was designed in 1871 by W. M. Fawcett to Maxwell's specifications and was erected through a gift from the seventh Duke of Devonshire, head of the Cavendish family.

James Clerk Maxwell
Physicist and Natural Philosopher

1. Background and Childhood

[1831-1841]

James Clerk Maxwell, the great nineteenth-century physicist, was a descendant of the Clerks of Penicuik, a family prominent in Edinburgh from 1670 on, who had twice intermarried during the eighteenth century with the heiresses of the Maxwells of Middlebie, illegitimate offspring of the eighth Lord Maxwell. His father, John Clerk (Maxwell), younger brother of Sir George Clerk, M.P., inherited the Middlebie property and took the name Maxwell in consequence of some earlier legal manipulations which prevented the two family properties being held together. The estate, some 1,500 acres of farmland near Dalbeattie in Galloway (southwestern Scotland), descended to Maxwell; and much of his scientific writing was done there. Maxwell's mother was Frances Cay, daughter of R. Hodshon Cay, a member of a Northumbrian family residing in Edinburgh. She died when he was eight years old. On both parents' sides Maxwell inherited intellectual traditions connected with the law, as was common in cultivated Edinburgh families. John Clerk Maxwell had been trained as an advocate, but his chief interest was in practical, technical matters. He was a fellow of the Royal Society of Edinburgh and published one scientific paper, a proposal for an automatic-feed printing press. Maxwell's father was a Presbyterian and his mother an Episcopalian. Maxwell himself maintained a strong Christian faith, with a strain of mysticism which has affinities with the religious traditions of the Galloway region, where he grew up.

Maxwell was born on 13 July 1831 in Edinburgh, where his parents were staying for medical attention during his mother's confinement. She was then in her fortieth year, having married late; one other child, a daughter, Elizabeth, born two years earlier, had survived only a few months. When all was well, the family returned to Glenlair House on the Maxwell estate, where amid huge festivities Mr. Maxwell ceremoniously planted a cutting from a copper beech tree, that beautiful variant species whose appearance at Kew Gardens some years earlier had startled the botanical world. The tree still flourishes.

The first ten years of Maxwell's life were almost all spent at Glenlair. Galloway even today is one of the least-known parts of Scotland. The modern traveler who arrives after a storm is struck by the rich green fields, with their stone walls and black Galloway cattle, and by the dramatic lights and shadows chasing across the waters, from the river

Urr that flows past Maxwell's home, to Loch Ken, near which at Parton kirk he is buried, and south to the Solway Firth, which separates Scotland from England. History too is visible, in the graceful ruins of Sweetheart Abbey, in Threave Castle near Glenlair, long disputed between the Maxwells and the Douglases, and in Caerlaverock Castle, the massive triangular shape guarding the Solway, of which Maxwell's ancestors were hereditary keepers. It was here that Mary Queen of Scots, accompanied by Lords Maxwell, Herries, and Fleming, embarked on her fatal journey to England, leaving royal gifts, among them a clock that descended to Maxwell. But without a leap of the imagination no twentieth-century eye can see the remoteness of Galloway in pre-railway times. The Glasgow-Edinburgh railway was opened in 1837 when Maxwell was six; the line through Dalbeattie nine years later. Till then the seventy miles to Glasgow were nearly a day's journey, and Edinburgh was two whole days away. Only in the previous thirty years had the countryside begun to be tamed. Older people remembered the marauding bands of gypsy cattle-reivers from the hills. When John Clerk Maxwell and his wife arrived in 1826, they were like pioneers. Stones had to be gathered from the fields before they could be worked. Mr. Maxwell himself drew up the designs for the house and supervised its construction from materials cut or quarried on the estate. Lewis Campbell, Maxwell's close friend and biographer, deftly caught the characters of the couple: John Clerk Maxwell, a large slow unwieldy man, thinking everything through to the last ingenious detail and then apt to be put out when plans went wrong; his wife, just as practical, "but her practicality was different from his. She was of a strong and resolute nature—as prompt as he was cautious and considerate—more peremptory but less easily perturbed . . . with blunt determination she entered heart and soul into that rustic life."[1] Once after a blasting accident, when her husband and everyone else were dithering about, she took charge and personally tended to the injured men during the long wait until the doctor's carriage rattled to the scene.

The Clerk family has been noted for its artistic talent as far back as the second Sir John Clerk (1676–1755), who had studied drawing and painting with William Mieris at Leyden and Andrea Imperiale in Rome. The talent happily descended to Maxwell's cousin Jemima, daughter of Mr. Maxwell's sister Isabella and James Wedderburn, one-time Solicitor General for Scotland. Jemima was eight years older than Maxwell. She married Lord Kelvin's friend Hugh Blackburn, professor of mathematics at Glasgow. During the period 1835 to 1844 she regularly visited Glenlair with her mother; her lively pictures of this period of Maxwell's youth have been preserved. The persons identified range from local notables, many with names that are still prominent in the region, to Maxwell's nurse Mrs. Fearon and Sam Murdoch and Sandy Fraser, sons of two of the cottagers on the estate. The social classes in Scotland were then much less separated than in England. Sam and Sandy were Maxwell's playmates from an early age. From them, he acquired the strong Gallowegian accent—so different from his parents' Edinburgh speech—that remained with him throughout his life; Lewis Campbell remarks that the rhyme of hasn't with pleasant in Maxwell's verse, and other such turns of phrase, recalled to those who knew him the quality of his speech.

The Edinburgh culture of Maxwell's parents and the remoteness of Galloway were the determining factors that shaped his education. Up to the time of his mother's death it was entirely in her hands. She taught him to read, encouraged (as did his father) his curiosity in all things, and took pride in his wonderful memory. At eight he could recite long passages from Milton, and knew by heart all 176 verses of Psalm 119. Then in 1839 she died of cancer—at the same age, and of the same disease, as her son forty years later. The shock to the boy was severe. Writing in 1868 to the astronomer William Huggins, whose mother had just then died, Maxwell remarked,

"Though my own mother was only eight years with me, and my father became my companion in all things, I felt her loss for many years, and can in some degree appreciate your happiness in having so long and so complete fellowship with your mother."

Superadded to the emotional loss was the problem of continuing the boy's education. For two years a tutor was tried, with results as bad as they could be. The tutor and Maxwell held different opinions about the merits of Latin grammar as an educational instrument, and Maxwell even then had the quality dryly characterized in Lewis Campbell's remark, "Few men, if any, would venture to argue or remonstrate with Maxwell when he had decided on a course of action in the council chamber of his own breast." The tutor, "a raw lad," endlessly provoked, did venture. Mr. Maxwell, whose many good qualities did not include the capacity to see inconvenient facts staring him in the face, did nothing; two years of war passed before Mrs. Maxwell's sister, Miss Jane Cay, on a visit to Glenlair, realized what was going on, and the tutor was dismissed. By then the damage was done. Maxwell's inward strength enabled him to survive setbacks that would have destroyed many people, but Campbell, whose psychological insight was acute, was surely right in tracing his odd indirection of manner to the circumstances following his mother's death.

2. Edinburgh

[1841-1850]

John Clerk Maxwell next decided to send his son to Edinburgh Academy. He himself remained generally in the country, and so for the next eight years Maxwell spent an uneasy existence, shuttled back and forth between his father at Glenlair and one or other of his two Edinburgh aunts, Mrs. Wedderburn and Miss Cay. The Academy had been founded in 1824 by a group that included Sir Walter Scott and Lord Cockburn, the lawyer and memorialist, to provide Scottish youth with a classical education along English lines. The headmaster, or Rector, to use his correct title, was an Oxford-educated Welshman, the Rev. John Williams, a fine scholar, popular with the boys because (in Maxwell's words to his father) "We have lots of jokes, and he speaks a great deal, and we have not so much monotonous parsing." Williams became prominent in the party that was out to anglicize the universities and rapidly made the Academy the leading school in Scotland, but even on home ground he did not always get his way. Most of his staff were Scotsmen with their own opinions about the activities of the Oxford interloper, not least among them James Gloag the mathematics master, according to C. G. Knott "a teacher of strenuous character and quaint originality," for whom, in the old Scottish tradition "mathematics was a mental and moral discipline." Knott recounts that:

> Once in the presence of the Rector, Gloag demanded a proof from one of the Rector's classical pets. After the Rector in a foolish assumption of knowledge had for some time encouraged the boy with such remarks as "Why my boy, don't you see it? Think a moment! It's quite easy, don't you know—perfectly simple!" Gloag in a moment of supreme triumph exclaimed "Naw Mr. Ractor, Sir, it's nott easy—the thing's impōssible, Sir—it's gross nonsense, Sir!"[2]

Thus early Maxwell was exposed to something that persisted through his career and had pervasive influence on his genius: the tension between Scottish and English educational ideals.

But first he encountered more mundane conflicts. He arrived at school, after the beginning of term, speaking the outlandish accents of Galloway and wearing clothes and shoes that his father, with his unquenchable faith in applied logic, had designed and made himself without regard for sartorial tradition. There followed a short sharp scene, described with eyewitness vividness by Lewis Campbell, in which Maxwell was encircled by a dozen of his schoolfellows, who proceeded to bash some right Edinburgh thinking into him. He returned to his aunt's home that day with his clothes torn to shreds, an air of brave amusement, and a new nickname, "Dafty." The name, which stuck to him through his schooldays and was not forgotten afterward, means strange rather than silly: "weirdo" might be closest to the modern idiom. Events were not all one-sided; a year or so later, in a scene oddly reminiscent of a tale about Newton, Maxwell rounded on a group of his tormentors and pummeled them into silence.

At the Academy Maxwell formed friendships with two very different boys, Lewis Campbell and P. G. Tait. Campbell, a nephew of Thomas Campbell, the poet, had a fine all-round intellect. Later he went on to Glasgow University and Balliol College, Oxford, where his tutor was Benjamin Jowett, afterward the most famous master of the college but at that time a young reforming don. Campbell imbibed Jowett's liberal Christian convictions, became a distinguished classical scholar in his own right, a pioneer in the linguistic analysis of texts, and a translator and commentator on Plato. Tait was a hardheaded mathematician and physicist; a year behind Maxwell in school, he went up to Cambridge two years earlier, was Senior Wrangler there in 1852, and in 1860 became professor of natural philosophy at Edinburgh. He is known to physicists as co-author with Sir William Thomson (Lord Kelvin) of the famous Thomson-Tait *Treatise on Natural Philosophy,* of which more later. The three-sided correspondence during the 1870's between Thomson, Tait, and Maxwell, much of it conducted on the new halfpenny postcards, is a wonderful—not to say a perplexing— quarry for the historian of nineteenth-century physics. In the correspondence Thomson and Tait were known as T and T', and Maxwell as dp/dt, since in Tait's *Sketch of Thermodynamics* (1868) one equation related to the second law of thermodynamics assumes the form $dp/dt = JCM$. Another symbol was T'' for John Tyndall, which Tait, who loathed Tyndall, explicated as denoting a quantity of the second order. Maxwell also sometimes called Thomson and Tait the "archiepiscopal pair," the archbishops of Canterbury and York at that time being Archibald Campbell Tait (himself another Edinburgh Academician) and William Thomson.

Maxwell's first three years at the Academy were outwardly undistinguished, though his contemporary letters to his father, some of which are reproduced in facsimile by his biographers, have a delightfully weird originality. His interest in geometry appeared in the models he made at home of the five regular solids; he discovered for himself the secondary polyhedra obtained by projecting the facets of the regular ones until alternate planes intersect. A later group of such figures, made in 1848, is preserved at Cambridge. Then suddenly, when he was fourteen, Maxwell produced his first scientific paper. It followed the efforts of D. R. Hay, a well-known decorative artist in Edinburgh, to find a method of drawing a perfect oval similar to the string property of the ellipse. Maxwell discovered that when the string used for the ellipse is folded back on itself n times toward one focus and m times toward the other, like the block and tackle of a crane, a true oval is formed, of the kind first studied by Descartes in connection with the refraction of light. Descartes had described ways of generating the curves, but Maxwell's method was new. His father excitedly showed the results to J. D. Forbes, the professor of natural philosophy at Edinburgh University, who secured publication in the *Proceedings of the Royal Society of Edinburgh*. Shortly afterward Maxwell wrote a remarkable manuscript, which is reproduced by his biographers, on the geometrical and optical properties of ovals and related curves of higher order. It afforded a foretaste of two of his lifelong characteristics: thoroughness and a predilection for geometrical reasoning. Both qualities, traditional in Scottish education, were powerfully reinforced in Maxwell by the teaching of James Gloag.

Some people have interpreted the paper on ovals

as evidence that Maxwell was an infant prodigy. This is a mistake. The idea was clever but it was the kind of clever idea that might have struck any very bright schoolboy who was familiar with the string property of the ellipse and had seen cranes at work; it was published only because Maxwell's father happened to know the right people. It was not deep mathematics like the marvelous theorem on conics that Pascal discovered at sixteen. In retrospect its greatest value lay in giving Maxwell an *entrée* to the scientific world of Edinburgh. From 1845 John Clerk Maxwell resumed his own attendance at meetings of the Royal Society of Edinburgh and regularly took his son along. During the remaining years at the Academy Maxwell swiftly advanced in all subjects but never achieved absolute dominance even in mathematics. In the examination for the Rector's Prize in 1847, Campbell was first, Tait second, and Maxwell sixth; the first three in mathematics were Tait, Campbell, Maxwell, in that order. Campbell modestly said he never doubted Maxwell's superiority: "he seemed to be in the heart of the subject [geometry] when [others] were only at the boundary." Yet the examination result did not mean that Maxwell lacked competitive drive. Later, as an undergraduate at Edinburgh, he wrote two more scientific papers while still under twenty, but neither had the epoch-making quality of the papers that Thomson, who *was* a prodigy, wrote at a comparable age. The belief that scientific genius, especially of a mathematical kind, flowers early and withers by the age of thirty is a popular historical cliché. For Maxwell it is definitely false. The distinguishing quality of his intellect was its massive overarching strength: power always in reserve. Some papers of his twenties were excellent, but he did not truly hit his stride until his early thirties, and his most sophisticated mathematics came in his last two papers on gas theory, written in his late forties, just before he died.

Maxwell entered Edinburgh University in 1847 when he was sixteen, then the normal age of entry at Scottish universities. He continued for three years of the four-year course, working hard but not under pressure, doing mathematics, writing poetry, reading voraciously, laying up that formidable store of general knowledge which was to make one Cambridge friend, W. N. Lawson, note in his diary a few years later: "Maxwell as usual showed himself acquainted with every subject upon which the conversation turned. I never met a man like him. I do believe there is not a single subject on which he cannot talk, and talk well too, displaying always the most curious and out-of-the-way information."

At Edinburgh University Maxwell came under the influences of two strongly contrasted men, J. D. Forbes, the physicist and alpinist, whom he already knew, and Sir William Hamilton, the metaphysician. Forbes was an experimentalist, who is remembered for the invention of the seismometer, the discovery of polarization in radiant heat, and some pioneer work on the motion of glaciers. Hamilton (who must not be confused with his Irish mathematical namesake) held the chair of logic and metaphysics and both by force of personality and the tradition of his chair was considered the leading professor in the university. The two men were enemies, coming into collision on every university issue from the choice of a new colleague to the plan for a new pension fund; in one place only did they ever meet constructively, and that was in the mind of the seventeen-year-old Maxwell. Here their combined influence was magnificently beneficial. Forbes helped develop in Maxwell a practical down-to-earth interest in experimental technique rare in a theoretical physicist; he forced him to write clearly and communicated his own scholarly interest in the history of science. Hamilton's vast erudition, and brilliant if erratic critical powers, supplied exactly the right stimulus to awaken Maxwell (and numbers of other Edinburgh students) to fundamental questions. Many of his ideas are traceable in the interesting philosophical asides that occur throughout Maxwell's papers.

3. Cambridge, Aberdeen, London

[1850-1879]

In 1850 Maxwell went up to Cambridge and began the rigors of preparing for the mathematical tripos, then at the height of its competitive glory. He was nineteen, one year older than most entering undergraduates, his father's Scotch caution about English universities having delayed the inevitable transition. He spent one term at Peterhouse and then migrated to Trinity, in order, it is said, to avoid possible future competition with E. J. Routh for a Peterhouse fellowship. In his second year he became the fifteenth pupil in the private class of William Hopkins, the geophysicist and "wrangler-maker," a man now sadly disregarded by his university, though if a teacher is to be judged by his students, Hopkins, whose students included G. G. Stokes, Thomson, Arthur Cayley, N. M. Ferrers, Tait, Routh, and Maxwell, must be counted as one of the greatest in any generation. Maxwell also soon caught the eye of Stokes and found another philosophical mentor in William Whewell, the dominating master of Trinity, author of two famous treatises on the history and philosophy of the inductive sciences, among numerous other works.

While at Trinity College Maxwell formed friendships among the brilliant set of liberal classical scholars who graced its walls. He was elected a member of the famous "Apostles Club," the quasi-secret intellectual society founded in 1824 by a certain "immortal Tomlinson," ever thereafter toasted thus by the Apostles at their annual reunion. The society's early membership included figures as diverse as Alfred Tennyson, Richard Monckton Milnes, and one man beyond all whose fierce integrity permeated its spirit for many years: the young F. D. Maurice. In Maxwell's time the Apostles included J. F. Stephen, H. M. Butler, F. J. A. Hort, and a little later, Henry Sidgwick; afterward A. N. Whitehead, Bertrand Russell, John Maynard Keynes, and Lytton Strachey. Maxwell's biographers print portions of a dozen of the essays he read to the society between 1853 and 1856, some of which are of great value in comprehending his development. Maxwell graduated second wrangler and first Smith's prizeman (bracketed equal with Routh) in 1854. He became a fellow of Trinity in 1855 and remained in residence until 1856 when he took the chair of natural philosophy at Marischal College, Aberdeen. During his last three years at Cambridge Maxwell, with others of his circle at Trinity, became active in Maurice's Christian Socialist movement, helping to found the short-lived Cambridge Working Men's College. Maxwell's friend R. B. Litchfield was for many years secretary of the London Working Men's College. Maxwell continued regularly to teach evening classes for artisans in Aberdeen and London up to 1866; his contributions to adult education are seen also in two of his books, the *Theory of Heat* (1870) and *Matter and Motion* (1877), the first of which was advertised by the publishers, a little optimistically, as "within the comprehension of working men and suitable to their wants."

Maxwell spent four years at Marischal College. One of his students there, David Gill, afterward a distinguished astronomer and director of the observatory at the Cape of Good Hope, left a charming picture of the man whose teaching "influenced the whole of my future life":

> In those days there was no working physical laboratory at Aberdeen accessible to students, but simply an apparatus room containing the old-fashioned lecture models of levers, pulleys, pumps, windmills, steam engines, etc., with some balances, air pumps, tuning forks, an Atwood's machine, electric machines, a few galvanic batteries, etc., in glass cases; but access to this room was forbidden to students. After the lectures, however, Clerk Maxwell used to remain in the lecture-room for hours, with some three or four of us who desired to ask questions or discuss any points sug-

gested by himself or by ourselves, and would show us models of apparatus he had contrived and was experimenting with at the time, such as his precessional top, colour box, etc. These were hours of purest delight to me. Maxwell's lectures were, as a rule, most carefully arranged and written out—practically in a form fit for printing—and we were allowed to copy them. In lecturing he would begin reading his manuscript, but at the end of five minutes or so he would stop, remarking, "Perhaps I might explain this," and then he would run off after some idea which had just flashed upon his mind, thinking aloud as he covered the blackboard with figures and symbols, and generally outrunning the comprehension of the best of us. Then he would return to his manuscript, but by this time the lecture hour was nearly over and the remainder of the subject was dropped or carried over to another day. Perhaps there were a few experimental illustrations—and they very often failed—and to many it seemed that Clerk Maxwell was not a very good professor. But to those who could catch a few of the sparks that flashed as he thought aloud at the blackboard in lecture, or when he twinkled with wit and suggestion in after lecture conversation, Maxwell was supreme as an inspiration. The less imaginative side of instruction in mathematics and physics was admirably supplied by the extramural teaching of Dr. David Rennet.[3]

In 1858 Maxwell married Katherine Mary Dewar, daughter of the principal of Marischal College. She was seven years older than he. They had no children. The marriage was not without its strains. Mrs. Maxwell was jealous and difficult, and the ill health through which Maxwell nursed her from 1876 on was clearly of a neurotic kind. Earlier Maxwell had had an emotional involvement with his cousin Elizabeth Cay, a girl of great beauty and intelligence, which they had to terminate because of the perils of consanguinity in a family already inbred. Mrs. Maxwell's knowledge of the event, and of the Cays' contempt for her, cannot have helped. However, the story emanating from Mrs. Tait, and solemnly repeated by numerous writers since, that she attempted to stop Maxwell's scientific work is manifest nonsense. She helped him devotedly in his experiments on color vision and the kinetic theory of gases. Campbell, who would have given a shrewd assessment, could not in an official biography written during Mrs. Maxwell's lifetime. He includes a few serious letters from Maxwell to her and cites without quotation the much larger number of jolly ones written from Cambridge, "telling her of everything, however minute, which, if she had seen it, would have detained her eye, small social phenomena, grotesque or graceful (including the dress of lady-friends), together with the lighter aspects of the examinations; College customs, such as the "grace-cup"; his dealings with his coexaminers, and marks

55

of honour to himself which he knew would please her, though they were indifferent to him." Her one surviving letter to him, though odd, is affectionate enough.

In 1860 Maxwell was dismissed from his professorship at Aberdeen in the retrenchment that followed the union of Marischal College with King's College, the other university in Aberdeen. The incident roused angry feelings in the town; most people believed that it had been engineered by David Thompson, the professor of natural philosophy at King's College, who happened to be chairman of the commission presiding over the union of the two colleges. Actually Maxwell had already applied for the chair of natural philosophy at Edinburgh, from which Forbes had just retired. He was beaten in that competition by Tait but shortly afterward was appointed to the chair at King's College, London. He remained there until 1865, when he retired from regular academic life to write his celebrated *Treatise on Electricity and Magnetism* and to put into effect a long-cherished scheme for enlarging his house. The statement in the official history of King's College, London, that he was dismissed from his post there also, for failing to keep order in his classes, can be disproved on several grounds. Maxwell served as examiner or moderator in the Cambridge mathematical tripos during the years 1866, 1867, 1869, and 1870, instituting some widely praised reforms in the substance and style of the examinations. In 1871 he was appointed first professor of experimental physics at Cambridge and planned and developed the Cavendish Laboratory. He died of abdominal cancer on 5 November 1879.

4. Scientific Character and Early Work

Maxwell's place in the history of physics is fixed by his revolutionary investigations in electromagnetism and the kinetic theory of gases, along with substantial contributions in several other theoretical and experimental fields: (1) color vision, (2) the theory of Saturn's rings, (3) geometrical optics, (4) photoelasticity, (5) thermodynamics, (6) the theory of servomechanisms (governors), (7) viscoelasticity, (8) reciprocal diagrams in engineering structures, and (9) relaxation processes. He wrote four books and about one hundred papers. He was joint scientific editor with T. H. Huxley of the famous ninth edition of the *Encyclopaedia Britannica*, to which he contributed many articles. His *Unpublished Electrical Researches of the Hon. Henry Cavendish* (1879) is a classic of scientific editing, with a unique series of notes on investigations suggested by Cavendish's work.

Maxwell's electromagnetic theory of light has its foundations in the work of two earlier physicists: Michael Faraday and William Thomson. A comparison of the three men is interesting in many ways. Socially they could hardly have been more different. Faraday was an Englishman, the son of a blacksmith, a member of a small nonconformist sect, self-educated. Thomson and Maxwell were both Scotsmen, but from sharply contrasting milieus, Thomson being the son of the professor of mathematics at the University of Glasgow, and spending nearly all his life in that city, the hub of Scottish industry. If one wishes to characterize each man's genius with a single adjective, it is fair to describe Faraday as an accumulative thinker, Thomson as an inspirational thinker, and Maxwell as an architectural thinker. Faraday worked by gradually collecting arrays of facts, altering his ideas a little at a time, writing up progress every day in his carefully cross-referenced diary. His motto, "work, finish, publish," sums up his method, and if it seems a little pedestrian, one has only to examine his volumes of *Experimental Researches* to see its effectiveness. Thomson was a man of violent enthusiasms. He would take up a subject, work at it furiously for a few weeks, throw out a string of novel ideas, and then inexplicably drop everything and pass on. His best papers would have made perfect contributions to *Physical Review Letters:* their two or three pages containing a single brilliant idea might be the clue to the trickiest problem in physics or the start of the wildest of wild-goose chases. Until one has grasped Thomson's role as a catalyst to Maxwell, it is difficult really to appreciate his importance in the history of electromagnetism. Where he and even Faraday were weak was in the finished, organized working out of an idea, and it was there that Maxwell's genius was supreme. Maxwell's great papers are in total contrast to Thomson's. Seventy or eighty pages long (and tersely written at that), each is evidently the result of prolonged thinking, and each in its own way presents a complete view of its subject.

It was Maxwell's habit to work on different subjects in sequence, sometimes with an interval of several years between successive papers in the same field. Six years elapsed between his first and second papers on electricity (1855, 1861), twelve years between his second and third major papers on kinetic theory (1867, 1879). The account of his work must therefore be grouped by subject rather than in strict chronological order; a description of his remaining juvenile papers and the studies on color vision and Saturn's rings is useful in illustrating his intellectual development up to 1859.

Following his early work on ovals, Maxwell published two papers while at the University of Edinburgh and two more while an undergraduate at Cambridge. He continued to show a strong geometrical bent. Three of the four papers were on geometrical subjects. The first, "On the Theory of Rolling Curves" (1848), analyzed the differential geometry of families of curves generated like the cycloid, by one figure rolling on another. Another (1853) was a brief investigation in geometrical optics, leading to the beautiful discovery of the "fish-eye" lens. The third was "Transformation of Surfaces by Bending," which extended work begun by Gauss. The only paper from this period with a strictly physical subject was "On the Equilibrium of Elastic Solids," written in 1850 shortly before Maxwell went up to Cambridge. In 1847 he had been taken by his uncle John Cay to visit the private laboratory of the experimental optician William Nicol, from whom he received a pair of polarizing prisms. With these he investigated the phenomenon of induced double refraction in strained glass, which had been discovered in 1826 by another famous Scottish experimenter, Sir David Brewster. Maxwell's studies led him to the papers of Cauchy and Stokes. He developed a simple axiomatic formulation of the general theory of elasticity, solved various problems, and offered a conjectural explanation of induced double refraction based on strain functions. The alternative interpretation based on stress functions had been given earlier by F. E. Neumann, but Maxwell's theory was independent and better. The usefulness of photoelastic techniques in studying stress distributions in engineering structures is well known: retrospectively the paper is even more important as Maxwell's first encounter with continuum mechanics. Its significance for his researches on the electromagnetic field and (more surprisingly) gas theory will shortly appear.

Maxwell's paper on elastic solids was illustrated with beautiful hand-colored plates, which are not reproduced in the *Scientific Papers* but may be found in the original *Transactions of the Royal Society of Edinburgh,* volume 20. Maxwell was obviously proud of this work: in later years observant visitors to Glenlair would notice beside the main fireplace a potholder embroidered with colored patterns corresponding to the transmission of white light through a strained prism of square cross section.

5. Color Vision
[1850-1870]

Maxwell created the science of quantitative color-imetry. He proved that all colors may be matched by mixtures of three spectral stimuli, provided that subtraction as well as addition of stimuli is allowed. He revived Thomas Young's three-receptor theory of color vision and demonstrated that color blindness is due to the ineffectiveness of one or more receptors. He also projected the first color photograph and made other noteworthy contributions to physiological optics.

Credit for reviving Young's theory of vision is usually given to Helmholtz. His claim cannot be sustained. The paper it is based on, published in 1852, contained useful work, but Helmholtz overlooked the essential step of putting negative quantities in the color equations and explicitly rejected the three-receptor hypothesis; and although Grassmann in 1854 pointed out fallacies in his reasoning, there is no evidence that Helmholtz followed the argument through to a conclusion until after Maxwell's work appeared. Artists had indeed known centuries before

Maxwell or Helmholtz that the three so-called primary pigments, red, yellow, and blue, yield any desired hue by mixture; but several things clouded interpretation of the phenomena and hindered acceptance of Young's idea. One was the weight of Newton's claim that the prismatic spectrum contains seven primary colors rather than three. Another was the cool reception given to Young's theory of light, which extended to his theory of vision. The course of speculation between Young and Maxwell has never been clearly charted. In Britain the three-receptor theory did nearly gain acceptance during the 1820's. It was favorably discussed by John Herschel and Dalton as well as by Young: Herschel in particular suggested that Dalton's red blindness might come from the absence of one of Young's three receptors.[4] A curious complication supervened, however. During the 1830's Brewster performed experiments with absorption filters by which he claimed to demonstrate the existence of three kinds of light, distributed in various proportions throughout the spectrum. Color according to him was thus an objective property of light, not a physiological function of the human eye. Brewster's interpretations were founded on his stubborn belief in the corpuscular theory of light, but the experiments seemed good and were accepted even by Herschel until Helmholtz eventually traced the effects to imperfect focusing. During the same period from 1830 on, wide general progress was made in physiological optics throughout Europe, in which the names of Purkinje, Haidinger, Johannes Müller, and Wartmann are memorable. In Britain the first statistical survey of color deficiency was conducted by George Wilson of Edinburgh—the chemist, and biographer of Cavendish—who brought to the subject a nice touch of topical alarmism through his lurid warnings about the dangers inherent in nighttime railway signaling. It was in an appendix to Wilson's monograph *On Colour Blindness* (1855) that Maxwell's first account of his researches appeared.

Maxwell began experiments on color mixing in 1849 in Forbes's laboratory at Edinburgh. At that time Edinburgh was unusually rich in students of color: besides Forbes, Wilson, and Brewster, there were William Swan, a physician interested in the eye, and D. R. Hay, who, in addition to his work in the geometry of design, had written a book entitled *Nomenclature of Colours* (1839) and supplied Forbes and Maxwell with tinted papers and tiles for their investigations. The experiments consisted in observing hues generated by colored sectors on a rapidly spinning disk. Forbes first repeated a standard experiment in which a series of colors representing those of the spectrum combine to give gray. He then tried to produce gray from combinations of red, yellow, and blue but failed—"and the reason was found to be, that blue and yellow do not make green, but a pinkish tint, when neither prevails in the combination."[5] No addition of red to this could produce a neutral tint.

Using a top with adjustable sectors of tinted paper, Forbes and Maxwell went on to obtain quantitative color equations, employing red, blue, and *green* as primaries. Interestingly, Young, in one little-known passage, had made the same substitution.[6] The standard rules for mixing pigments were explained by Maxwell, and independently by Helmholtz, as a secondary process, with the pigments acting as filters to light reflected from the underlying surface.

In 1854, after his graduation from Cambridge, Maxwell was able to resume these researches, which Forbes had been compelled by a severe illness to abandon. He improved the top by adding a second set of adjustable sectors of smaller diameter than the first, to make accurate color comparisons, and obtained equations for several groups of observers which could be manipulated algebraically in a consistent manner. For color-deficient observers only two variables were needed. Maxwell then went on to prove that Newton's method of displaying colors on a circle with white at the center implicitly satisfies the three-receptor theory, since it is equivalent to representing each color datum by a point in a three-dimensional space. With the experimental results plotted on a triangle having red, blue, and green corners, after the method of Young and Forbes, there is a white point w inside and an ordered curve of spectral colors outside the triangle very similar to Newton's circle. Adapting terminology from D. R. Hay, Maxwell distinguished three new variables—hue (spectral color), tint (degree of saturation), shade (intensity of illumination)—corresponding to "angular position with respect to w, distance from w, and coefficient [of intensity]." There is an easy transformation from these variables and to the representation of colors as a sum of three primaries: hence "the relation between the two methods of reducing the elements to three becomes a matter of geometry."[7] All this is most modern. In later correspondence with Stokes (1862), Maxwell described manipulations of color coordinates to reduce data from different observers to a common white point. The advantages of this procedure were also pointed out by C. J. Monro in a letter to Maxwell, dated 3 March 1871, which was published in Campbell and Garnett's *Life of James Clerk Maxwell* (1882), although other workers in colorimetry entirely ignored the idea until Ives and Guild rediscovered it fifty years later.[8]

To go further, a new instrument less susceptible than the color top to conditions of illumination and properties of paper was called for. Accordingly Maxwell devised what he called his "colour-box," in which mixtures of spectral stimulants were directly compared with a matching white field. The original version, perfected in 1858, consisted of two wooden boxes, each about three feet long, joined at an angle, containing a pair of refracting prisms at the inter-section. An eyepiece was placed at one end; at the other were three slits, adjustable in position and aperture, which could be set at positions corresponding to any three wavelengths A, B, C in the spectrum formed by projecting white light through the eyepiece. By the principle of reciprocity, white light entering the slits yielded mixtures of A, B, C at the eyepiece, with intensities determined by the widths of the slits. Light from the same source (a sheet illuminated by sunlight) entered another aperture and was reflected past the edge of the second prism to the eyepiece, where the observer saw, side by side, two fields which he could match in hue and intensity. The spectrum locus determined by Maxwell's observer K (his wife) is shown in Figure 1, together with the results of König and Abney (1903, 1913) and the 1931 standard observer. The Maxwells come out of the comparison rather well. Maxwell designed two other "colour-boxes" on the same general principle. The second was made portable by the use of folded optics on the principle afterward adapted to the spectroscope by Littrow. The third gave hues of exceptional spectral purity by adopting a "double monochromator" principle, illuminating the slits with the spectrum from a second train of prisms symmetrically disposed rather than with direct sunlight. With it Maxwell studied variations of color sensitivity across the retina, a subject he had become interested in through his observations of the "Maxwell spot."

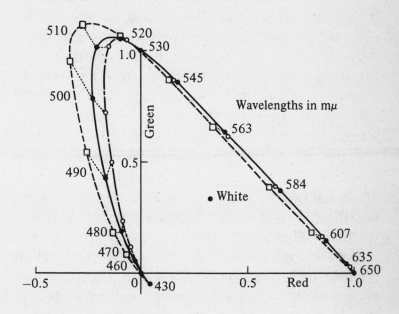

FIGURE 1. Spectrum loci determined by different experimenters.

——— ○ Maxwell 1860 (observer *K*)

- - - □ König, Abney 1903, 1913 (recalculated Weaver)

——— ● C.I.E. standard observer 1931 (Wright, Guild)

Most people, when they look at an extended source of polarized light, intermittently perceive a curious pair of yellow structures resembling a figure eight, with purple wings at the waist. These are the "brushes" discovered by Haidinger in 1844. They may be seen especially clearly by looking at a blue surface through a Nicol prism. Maxwell studied them with the prisms he had received from Nicol; and at the British Association meeting of 1850 he proposed attributing them to a polarizing structure in the yellow spot on the retina, a hypothesis which brought him into an amusing confrontation with Brewster, who attributed them to the cornea. Maxwell's explanation is now accepted. In 1855 he noticed, in the blue region of the spectrum formed by looking through a prism at a vertical slit, an elongated dark spot which moved up and down with the eye and possessed the same polarizing structure as Haidinger's brushes. This is the Maxwell spot. Later his wife discovered that she could not see the spot, there being almost no yellow pigment on her retinas. Noticing also a large discrepancy between her white point and his, Maxwell then found that his own color matches contained much less blue in the extrafoveal region and he proceeded to investigate variations of sensitivity across the retina for a large number of observers. He was able to exhibit the yellow spot—as he wrote to C. J. Monro in 1870—to "all who have it,—and all have it except

Col. Strange, F. R. S., my late father-in-law and my wife,—whether they be Negroes, Jews, Parsees, Armenians, Russians, Italians, Germans, Frenchmen, Poles, etc."[9] Summaries of the work appeared in two brief papers and in a delightful correspondence with Monro, which also contains an interesting discussion on differences in color nomenclature between ancient and modern languages.

In 1861 Maxwell projected the first trichromatic color photograph at the Royal Institution before an audience which included Faraday. The subject was a tartan ribbon photographed through red, green, and blue filters by Thomas Sutton, a colleague at King's College, London, and then projected through the same filters. An odd fact which remained without explanation for many years was that the wet collodion plates used should not have given any red image, since that photographic process is completely insensitive to red. Yet contemporary descriptions make it clear that the colors were reproduced with some fidelity. In 1960 R. M. Evans and his colleagues at Kodak Research Laboratories, in a first-class piece of historical detective work, established that the red dyes in Maxwell's ribbon also reflected ultraviolet light in a region just coinciding with a pass band in the ferric thiocyanate solution used as a filter. The "red" image was really obtained with ultraviolet light! The hypothesis is confirmed by the fact that the original red plate preserved at Cambridge is slightly out of focus, although Sutton carefully refocused the camera for visible red light. A repetition of the experiment under modern conditions gave a "surprisingly colorful reproduction of the original scene."[10]

6. Saturn's Rings

[1855-1859]

In 1855 the topic of the fourth Adams prize at Cambridge was announced as an investigation of the motions and stability of the rings of Saturn. Some calculations on Saturn's rings, treated as solid bodies, had been given as early as 1787 by Laplace. He established that a uniform rigid ring would disintegrate unless (1) it is rotating at a speed where the centrifugal force balances the attraction of the planet and (2) the ratio ρ_r/ρ_s of its density to the density of Saturn exceeds a critical value 0.8, such that the attractions between inner and outer portions of the ring exceed the differences between centrifugal and gravitational forces at different radii. Also, the motions of a uniform ring are dynamically unstable: any displacement from equilibrium leads to an increased attraction in the direction of displacement, precipitating the ring against the planet. Laplace conjectured, however, that the motion is somehow stabilized by irregularities in the mass distribution; and in his dogmatic way asserted that the rings of Saturn are irregular solid bodies. That was where the

73

theory still stood in 1855; meanwhile, a new dark ring and further divisions in the existing rings had been observed, along with some evidence for slow changes in the overall dimensions of the system during the 200 years since its discovery. The examiners, James Challis, Samuel Parkinson, and William Thomson, called for explanations of each point and an investigation of dynamical stability on the hypothesis that the rings are: (1) solid, (2) fluid, (3) composed of "masses of matter not mutually coherent."[11] These were the questions on which Maxwell spent much time between 1855 and 1859 in the essay to which the prize was awarded.

Maxwell took up first the theory of the solid ring where Laplace had left it, and determined conditions for stability of a ring of arbitrary shape. Forming equations of motion in terms of the potential at the center of Saturn due to the ring, he obtained two restrictions on the first derivatives of the potential for uniform motion, and then, by a Taylor expansion, three more conditions on the second derivatives for stable motion. Maxwell next transformed these results into conditions on the first three coefficients of a Fourier series in the mass distribution. He was able to show that almost every conceivable ring was unstable except the curious special case of a uniform ring loaded at one point with a mass between 4.43 and 4.87 times the remaining mass. There the uneven distribution makes the total attraction act toward a point outside the ring in such a way that the instabilities affecting the moment of inertia are counteracted by a couple which alters the angular momentum. But such a ring would collapse under the uneven stress, and its lopsidedness would be plainly visible. The hypothesis of a solid ring is untenable.

In considering nonrigid rings Maxwell again utilized Fourier's theorem, but in a different way, examining the stability of various rings by expanding disturbances in their form into a series of waves. He took as a starting model, with which more complex structures could later be compared, a ring of solid satellites, equally spaced and all of equal mass. The motions may be resolved into four components: rotation about Saturn with constant angular velocity ω and small displacement ρ, σ, ζ in directions radial, tangential, and normal to the plane of the ring. Normal displacements of any satellite are manifestly stable, for the components of attraction to the other bodies always constitute a restoring force. Tangential disturbances might be expected to be unstable, since the attractions to neighboring satellites are in the direction of displacement; but Maxwell discovered that radial and tangential waves of a given order may be coupled together in a stable manner because the radial motions generate Coriolis forces through the rotation about the planet, which counterbalance the gravitational forces due to tangential motions. Detailed analysis revealed four kinds of waves, grouped in two pairs, all of which are stable if the mass of the central body is great enough. The motions are rather complicated; and Maxwell, "for the edification of sensible image worshippers,"[12] had a mechanical model constructed to illustrate them in a ring of thirty-six satellites. Waves of the first two kinds move in opposite directions with respect to a point on the rotating ring, with a velocity nearly equal to ω/n, where ω is the angular velocity of the ring and n the number of undulations. Thus if there are five undulations the wave velocity is 1/5 of the ring velocity. Each satellite describes an elliptical path about its mean position in a sense opposite to the rotation of the ring itself, the major axis of the ellipse being approximately twice the minor axis and lying near the tangential plane. If the number of satellites is μ, the highest-order waves, which are most likely to disrupt the ring, have $\mu/2$ undulations. The stability criterion is

$$S > 0.4352\mu^2 R, \qquad (1)$$

S and R being the masses of Saturn and the ring. Stability is determined by tangential forces; the parameter defining them must lie between 0 and $0.07\omega^2$.

For rings of finite breadth Maxwell's procedure was to examine simplified models which bracket the true situation. He began with rings whose inner and outer parts are so strongly bound together that they rotate uniformly. Such rings may be called semirigid. They are evidently subject to Laplace's criterion of cohesion $\rho_r/\rho_s > 0.8$ but, like a ring of satellites, are also subject to conditions of stability against tangential disturbances. Maxwell established that tangential forces disrupt a semirigid ring of particles unless $\rho_r/\rho_s < 0.003$ and one of incompressible fluid unless $\rho_r/\rho_s < 0.024$. Since neither is compatible with Laplace's criterion, neither kind of semirigid ring is stable. Various arguments then disposed of other gaseous and liquid rings, leaving as the only stable structure concentric circles of small satellites, each moving at a speed appropriate to its distance from Saturn. Such rings cannot be treated independently: they attract one another. Maxwell presented a lengthy investigation of mutual perturbations between two rings. Usually they are stable; but at certain radii waves of different order may come into resonance and cause disruption, making particles fly off in all directions and collide with other rings. Maxwell estimated the rate of loss of energy and concluded that the whole system of rings would slowly spread out, as the observations indicated. He did not then study the general problem of motion among colliding bodies, but his unpublished manuscripts include one from 1863 applying the statistical methods that he

77

later developed in the kinetic theory of gases to Saturn's rings.

In 1895 A. A. Belopolsky and J. Keeler independently confirmed the differential rotation of the rings by spectroscopic observations. Later the gaps between successive rings were attributed to resonances between orbital motions of the primary satellites of Saturn and local ring oscillations. More recently A. F. Cook and F. A. Franklin, using kinetic theory techniques, have shown that heat generated in collisions makes the rings expand in thickness unless it is removed by radiation, and have obtained closer restrictions on structure and density. Maxwell's density limit $\rho_r/\rho_s > 0.003$ has sometimes been interpreted as a limit on the actual rings; in reality it applies only to semirigid rings, where stability depends on tangential forces. With differential rotation the tangential waves are heavily damped and stability depends on radial motions. The true upper limit on ρ_r/ρ_s appears to be in the range 0.04 to 0.20. Spectroscopic evidence suggests the particles may be crystals of ice or carbon dioxide.[13]

The essay on Saturn's rings illustrates Maxwell's debt to Cambridge as sharply as the experiments on color vision reveal his debt to Edinburgh. It also established his scientific maturity. Success with a classical problem of such magnitude gave a mathematical self-assurance vitally important to his later work. Many letters testify to the concentrated effort involved, not the least interesting amongst them being one to a Cambridge friend, H. R. Droop: "I am very busy with Saturn on top of my regular work. He is all remodelled and recast, but I have more to do to him yet for I wish to redeem the character of mathematicians and make it intelligible."[14] To the graceful literary style and analytical clarity established there, two further broad qualities were added in Maxwell's work over the next two decades. The great papers of the 1860's continued at much the same level of analytical technique, with epoch-making advances in physical and philosophic insight. The books and articles of the 1870's display growing mastery of mathematical abstraction in the use of matrices, vectors and quaternions, Hamiltonian dynamics, special functions, and considerations of symmetry and topology. The contrasting ways in which these different phases of Maxwell's mature researches reflect his interaction with his contemporaries and his influence on the next scientific generation form a fascinating study which has not yet received due attention.

7. Electromagnetism: Foundations of Maxwell's Theory

Maxwell's electrical researches began a few weeks after his graduation from Cambridge in 1854, and ended in 1879, just before his death, with a referee's report on a paper by G. F. FitzGerald. They fall into two broad cycles, with 1868 roughly the dividing point: the first a period of five major papers on the foundations of electromagnetic theory, the second a period of extension with the *Treatise on Electricity and Magnetism*, the *Elementary Treatise on Electricity*, and a dozen shorter papers on special problems. The position of the *Treatise* is peculiar. Most readers come to it expecting a systematic exposition of its author's ideas which makes further reference to earlier writings unnecessary. With many writers the expectation might be legitimate; with Maxwell it is a mistake. In a later conversation he remarked that the aim of the *Treatise* was not to expound his theory finally to the world but to educate himself by presenting a view of the stage he had reached.[15] This is a clue well worth pondering. The truth is that by 1868 Maxwell had already begun to think beyond his theory. He saw electricity not as just another branch of physics but as a subject of unique strategic importance, "as an aid to the interpretation of nature . . . and promoting the progress of science."[16] Wishing, therefore, to follow up questions with wider scientific ramifications, he gave the *Treatise* a loose-knit structure, organized on historical and experimental rather than deductive lines. Ideas are exhibited at different phases of growth in different places; different sections are developed independently, with gaps, inconsistencies, or even flat contradictions in argument. It is a studio rather than a finished work of art. The studio, being Maxwell's, is tidily arranged; and once one has grasped what is going on, it is wonderfully instructive to watch the artist at work; but anyone who finds himself there unawares is courting bewilderment, the more so if he overlooks Maxwell's advice to read the four parts of the *Treatise* in parallel rather than in sequence. It is, for example, disconcerting to be told on reaching section 585, halfway through volume II, that Maxwell is now about to "begin again from a new foundation without any assumption except those of the dynamical theory as stated in Chapter VII." Similar difficulties occur throughout. The next fifty years endorsed Maxwell's judgment about the special importance of electricity to physics as a whole. His premature death occurred just as his ideas were gaining adherents and he was starting an extensive revision of the *Treatise*. Not the least unfortunate consequence was that the definitive exposition of his theory which he intended was never written.

Seen in retrospect, the course of physics up to about 1820 is a triumph of the Newtonian scientific program. The "forces" of nature—heat, light, electricity, magnetism, chemical action—were being progressively reduced to instantaneous attractions and repulsions between the particles of a series of fluids. Magnetism and static electricity were already known to obey inverse-square laws similar to the law of gravitation. The first forty years of the nineteenth century saw a growing reaction against such a division of phenomena in favor of some kind of "correlation of forces." Oersted's discovery of electromagnetism in 1820 was at once the first vindication and the most powerful stimulus of the new tendency, yet at the same time it was oddly disturbing. The action he observed between an electric current and a magnet differed from known phenomena in two essential ways: it was developed by electricity in motion, and the magnet was neither attracted to nor repelled by—but set transversely to—the wire carrying the current. To such a strange phenomenon widely different reactions were possible. Faraday took it as a new irreducible fact by which his other ideas were to be shaped. André Marie Ampère and his followers sought to reconcile it with existing views about instantaneous action at a distance.

Shortly after Oersted's discovery Ampère discovered that a force also exists between two electric currents and put forward the brilliant hypothesis that all magnetism is electrical in origin. In 1826 he established a formula (not to be confused with the one attached to his name in textbooks) which reduced the known magnetic and electromagnetic phenomena to an inverse-square force along the line joining two current elements idl, $i'dl'$ separated by a distance r,

$$F_{ii'} = \frac{ii' \, dl \, dl'}{r^2} \, G, \qquad (2)$$

where G is a complex geometrical factor involving the angles between r, dl, and dl'. In 1845 F. E. Neumann derived the potential function corresponding to Ampère's force and extended the theory to electromagnetic induction. Another extension developed by Wilhelm Weber was to combine Ampère's law with the law of electrostatics to form a new theory, which also accounted for electromagnetic induction, treating the electric current as the flow of two equal and opposite groups of charged particles, subject to a force whose direction was always along the line joining two particles e, e', but whose magnitude depended on their relative velocity $\dot{r}$ and relative acceleration $\ddot{r}$ along that line,

83

$$F_{ee'} = \frac{ee'}{r^2} \left[1 - \frac{1}{c^2} (\dot{r}^2 - 2r\ddot{r}) \right], \qquad (3)$$

c being a constant with dimensions of velocity. In 1856 Kohlrausch and Weber determined c experimentally by measuring the ratio of electrostatic to electrodynamic forces. Its value in the special units of Weber's theory was about two-thirds the velocity of light. Equations (2) and (3) and Neumann's potential theory provided the starting points for almost all the work done in Europe on electromagnetic theory until the 1870's.

The determining influences on Maxwell were Faraday and William Thomson. Faraday's great discoveries—electromagnetic induction, dielectric phenomena, the laws of electrochemistry, diamagnetism, magneto-optical rotation—all sprang from the search for correlations of forces. They formed, in Maxwell's words, "the nucleus of everything electric since 1830."[17] His contributions to theory lay in the progressive extension of ideas about lines of electric and magnetic force. His early discovery of electromagnetic rotations (the first electric motor) made him skeptical about attractive and repulsive forces, and his ideas rapidly advanced after 1831 with his success in describing electromagnetic induction by the motion of lines of magnetic force through the inductive circuit. In studying dielectric and electrolytic processes

84

he imagined (wrongly) that their transmission in curved lines could not be reconciled with the hypothesis of direct action at a distance, attributing them instead to successive actions of contiguous portions of matter in the space between charged bodies. In his work on paramagnetism and diamagnetism he conceived the notion of magnetic conductivity (permeability); and finally, in the most brilliant of of his conceptual papers, written in 1852, when he was sixty, he extended the principle of contiguous action in a general qualitative description of magnetic and electromagnetic phenomena, based on the assumption that lines of magnetic force have the physical property of shortening themselves and repelling each other sideways. A quantitative formulation of the last hypothesis was given by Maxwell in 1861.

Thomson's contribution began in 1841, while he was an undergraduate at Cambridge. His first paper established a formal analogy between the equations of electrostatics and the equations for flow of heat. Consider a point source of heat P embedded in a homogeneous conducting medium. Since the surface area of a sphere is $4\pi r^2$, the heat flux ϕ through a small area dS at a distance r from P is proportional to $1/r^2$ in analogy with Coulomb's electrostatic law; thus by appropriate substitution a problem in electricity may be transposed into one in the theory of heat. Originally Thomson used the analogy as a

85

source of analytical technique; but in 1845 he went on to examine and dispose of Faraday's widely accepted claim that dielectric action cannot be reconciled with Coulomb's law and, conversely, to supply the first exact mathematical description of lines of electric force. Later Thomson and Maxwell between them established a general similitude among static vector fields subject to the conditions of continuity and incompressibility, proving that identical equations describe (1) streamlines of frictionless incompressible fluids through porous media, (2) lines of flow of heat, (3) current electricity, and (4) lines of force in magneto-statics and electrostatics.

Since it was Thomson's peculiar genius to generate powerful disconnected insights rather than complete theories, much of his work is best described piecemeal along with Maxwell's; but certain of his ideas from the 1840's may first be mentioned, notably the method of electric images, a second formal analogy between magnetic forces and rotational strains in an elastic solid, and, most important, the many applications of energy principles to electricity which followed his involvement with thermodynamics. Amongst other things Thomson is responsible for the standard expressions $\frac{1}{2}Li^2$ and $\frac{1}{2}CV^2$ for energy in an in-ductance and in a condenser. He and (independently) Helmholtz also applied energy principles to give an extraordinarily simple derivation of Neumann's induction equation. It so happened that the discussion of energy principles had a curious two-sided impact on Weber's hypothesis. In 1846 Helmholtz presented an argument which seemed to show that the hypothesis was inconsistent with the principle of conservation of energy. His conclusion was widely accepted and formed one of the grounds on which Maxwell opposed the theory, but in 1869 Weber succeeded in rebutting it. By then, however, Maxwell had developed his theory, and the implication of the Thomson-Helmholtz argument had become clearer: that any theory which is consistent with energy principles automatically predicts induction. In retrospect, therefore, although Helmholtz was wrong in his first criticism, the agreement between Weber's theory and experiment was also less compelling than Weber and his friends had supposed.

Maxwell's first paper, "On Faraday's Line of Force" (1855–1856), was divided into two parts, with supplementary examples. Its origin may be traced in a long correspondence with Thomson, edited by Larmor in 1936.[18] Part 1 was an exposition of the analogy between lines of force and streamlines in an incompressible fluid. It contained one notable extension to Thomson's treatment of the subject and also an illuminating opening discourse on the philosophical significance of analogies between different branches of physics. This was a theme to which Maxwell returned more than once. His biographers print in full an essay entitled "Analogies in Nature," which he read a few months later, during February 1856, to the Apostles Club at Cambridge; this puts the subject in a wider setting and deserves careful reading despite its involved and cryptic style. Here, as elsewhere, Maxwell's metaphysical speculation discloses the influence of Sir William Hamilton, specifically of Hamilton's Kantian view that all human knowledge is of relations rather than of things. The use Maxwell saw in the method of analogy was twofold. It cross-fertilized technique between different fields, and it served as a golden mean between analytic abstraction and the method of hypothesis. The essence of analogy (in contrast with identity) being partial resemblance, its limits must be recognized as clearly as its existence; yet analogies may help in guarding against too facile commitment to a hypothesis. The analogy of an electric current to two phenomena as different as conduction of heat and the motion of a fluid should, Maxwell later observed, prevent physicists from hastily assuming that "electricity is either a substance like water, or a state of agitation like heat."[19] The analogy is geometrical: "a similarity between relations, not a similarity between the things related."[20]

Maxwell improved the presentation of the hydro-dynamic analogy chiefly by considering the resistive medium through which the fluid moves. When an incompressible fluid goes from one medium into another of different porosity, the flow is continuous but a pressure difference develops across the boundary. Also, when one medium is replaced by another of different porosity, equivalent effects may be obtained formally by introducing appropriate sources or sinks of fluid at the boundary. These results were an important aid to calculation and helped in explaining several processes that occur in magnetic and dielectric materials. Another step was to consider a medium in which the porosity varies with direction. The necessary equations had been supplied by Stokes in a paper on the conduction of heat in crystals. They led to the remarkable conclusion that the vector **a** which defines the direction of fluid motion is not in general parallel to **α**, the direction of maximum pressure gradient. The two functions are linked by the equation

$$\mathbf{a} = \mathbf{K}\alpha, \tag{4}$$

where **K** is a tensor quantity describing the porosity. Applying the analogy to magnetism, Maxwell distinguished two vectors, the magnetic induction and the magnetic force, to which he later attached the symbols **B** and **H**. The parallel quantities in current electricity were the current density **I** and the electromotive intensity **E**. The distinction between **B** and **H** provided the key to a description of "magnecrystallic induction," a force observed in crystalline magnetic materials by Faraday. Maxwell later identified the two quantities with the two definitions of magnetic force that Thomson had found to be required in developing parallel magnetostatic and electromagnetic theories of magnetism. The question of the two magnetic vectors **B** and **H** has disturbed several generations of students of electromagnetism. Maxwell's discussion gives a far clearer starting point than anything to be found in the majority of modern textbooks on the subject.

This physical distinction based on the hydrodynamic analogy led Maxwell to make an important mathematical distinction between two classes of vector functions, which he then called "quantities" and "intensities," later "fluxes" and "forces." A flux **a** is a vector subject to the continuity equation and is integrated over a surface; a force **α** (in Maxwell's generalized sense of the term) is a vector usually, but not always, derivable from a single-valued potential function and is integrated along a line. The functions **B** and **I** are fluxes; **H** and **E** are forces.

The close parallel that exists between electric currents and magnetic lines of force, which had been seen qualitatively by Faraday, was the concluding theme of Part 1 of Maxwell's paper. Part 2 covered electromagnetism proper. In it Maxwell developed a new formal theory of electromagnetic processes. The starting point was an identity established by

90

Ampère and Gauss between the magnetic effects of a closed electric current and those of a uniformly magnetized iron shell of the same perimeter. In analytic method the discussion followed Thomson's "Mathematical Theory of Magnetism" (1851), as well as making extensive use of a theorem first proved by Thomson in 1847, in a letter to Stokes, and first published by Stokes as an examination question in the Smith's prize paper taken by Maxwell in February 1854. This was the well-known equality (Stokes's theorem) between the integral of a vector function around a closed curve and the integral of its curl over the enclosed surface. The original analysis given by Maxwell was Cartesian, but since in 1870 he himself introduced the terms "curl," "divergence," and "gradient" to denote the relevant vector operations, the notation may legitimately be modernized. The relationship between the flux and force vectors $\mathbf{a}$ and α contained in equation (4) has already been discussed. Pursuing a line of analysis started by Thomson, Maxwell now proceeded to show that any flux vector $\mathbf{a}$ may be related to a second, distinct force vector α' through the equation

$$\mathbf{a} = \operatorname{curl} \alpha' + \operatorname{grad} \beta, \qquad (5)$$

where β is a scalar function. Applying (4), (5) and other equations, Maxwell obtained a complete set of equations between the four vectors $\mathbf{E}$, $\mathbf{I}$, $\mathbf{B}$, $\mathbf{H}$, which describe electric currents and magnetic lines of force. He then went on to derive another vector function, for which he afterward used the symbol **A**, such that

$$\mathbf{B} = \text{curl } \mathbf{A} + \text{grad } \varphi, \qquad (6)$$

where the second term on the right-hand side may, in the absence of free magnetic poles, be eliminated by appropriate change of variables. Maxwell proved that the electromotive force **E** developed during induction is $-\partial\mathbf{A}/\partial t$ and that the total energy of an electromagnetic system is $\int \mathbf{I} \cdot \mathbf{A} \, dV$. Thus the new function provided equations to represent ordinary magnetic action, electromagnetic induction, and the forces between closed currents. Maxwell called it the electrotonic function, following some speculations of Faraday's about a hypothetical state of stress in matter, the "electrotonic state." Later he identified it as a generalization of Neumann's electrodynamic potential and established other properties (to be discussed shortly).

The 1856 paper has been eclipsed by Maxwell's later work, but its originality and importance are greater than is usually thought. Besides interpreting Faraday's work and giving the electrotonic function, it contained the germ of a number of ideas which Maxwell was to revive or modify in 1868 and later: (1) an integral representation of the field equations

(1868), (2) the treatment of electrical action as analogous to the motion of an incompressible fluid (1869, 1873), (3) the classification of vector functions into forces and fluxes (1870), and (4) an interesting formal symmetry in the equations connecting **A**, **B**, **E**, and **H**, different from the symmetry commonly recognized in the completed field equations. The paper ended with solutions to a series of problems, including an application of the electrotonic function to calculate the action of a magnetic field on a spinning conducting sphere.

Maxwell's next paper, "On Physical Lines of Force" (1861–1862), began as an attempt to devise a medium occupying space which would account for the stresses associated by Faraday with lines of magnetic force. It ended with the stunning discovery that vibrations of the medium have properties identical with light. The original aim was one Maxwell had considered in 1856, and although he explicitly rejected any literal interpretation of the analogy between magnetic action and fluid motion, the meaning of the analogy can be extended by picturing a magnet as a kind of suction tube which draws in fluid ether at one end and expels it from the other. That idea had been suggested by Euler in 1761;[21] it leads to a most remarkable result first published by Thomson in 1870 but probably known to Maxwell earlier.[22] Geometrically the flow between two such tubes is identical with the lines of force between two magnets, but physically the actions are reciprocal: like ends of the tubes are *attracted* according to the inverse-square law; unlike ends are repelled. The difference is that in a fluid the Bernoulli forces create a pressure minimum where the streamlines are closest, while Faraday's hypothesis requires a pressure maximum.

The clue to to a medium having a right stress distribution came from an unexpected source. During the 1840's the engineer W. J. M. Rankine (who like Maxwell had been a student of Forbes's at Edinburgh) worked out a new theory of matter with applications to thermodynamics and the properties of gases, based on the hypothesis that molecules are small nuclei in an ethereal atmosphere, fixed in space but rotating at speeds proportional to temperature. In 1851 Thomson refereed one of Rankine's papers. He was then concerning himself with thermodynamics, but five years later it dawned on him that molecular rotation was just the thing to account for the magneto-optical effect.[23] Faraday had observed a slight rotation in the plane of polarization of light passing through a block of glass between the poles of a magnet. Using an analogy with a pendulum suspended from a spinning arm, Thomson concluded that the effect could be attributed to coupling between the ether vibrations and a spinning motion of the molecules of glass about the lines of force. Maxwell's theory of physical lines of force consisted in extending this hypothesis of rotation in the magnetic field from ordinary matter to an ether. The influence of Thomson and Rankine is established by direct reference and by Maxwell's use of Rankine's term "molecular vortices" in the titles of each of the four parts of the paper. The charm of the story is that barely twelve months had passed since Maxwell had given the death blow to Rankine's theory of gases through his own work on kinetic theory.

Consider an array of vortices embedded in incompressible fluid. Normally the pressure is identical in all directions, but rotation causes centrifugal forces which make each vortex contract longitudinally and exert radial pressure. This is exactly the stress distribution proposed by Faraday for physical lines of force. By making the angular velocity of each vortex proportional to the local magnetic intensity, Maxwell obtained formulas identical with the existing theories for forces between magnets, steady currents, and diamagnetic bodies. Next came the problem of electromagnetic induction. It required some understanding of the action of electric currents on the vortex medium. That tied in with another question: how could two adjacent vortices rotate freely in the same sense, since their surfaces move in opposite directions? Figure 2, reproduced from Part 2 of the paper with some drafting errors corrected, illustrates Maxwell's highly tentative solution. Each vortex is separated from its neighbors by a layer of minute particles, identified with electricity, counter-rotating like the idle wheels of a gear train.

On this view electricity, instead of being a fluid confined to conductors, becomes an entity of a new kind, disseminated through space. In conductors it is free to move (though subject to resistance);

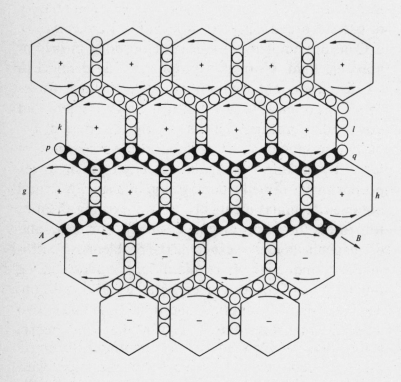

FIGURE 2. Model of molecular vortices and electric particles (1861).

in insulators (including the ultimate insulator, space) it remains fixed. The magnetic and inductive actions of currents are then visualized as follows. Imagine a horizontal wire incorporating the line of particles *AB* in figure 2. When a current flows, the moving particles make the adjacent vortices *gh* rotate; these engage the layer of particles *pr,* which, being fixed in space, act on the next vortices *kl,* and so on, until an infinite series of vortex rings, which constitute lines of force, fills the surrounding space. For induction, consider a second wire *CD* (not shown) parallel to the first one, and having finite electrical resistance. A steady current in *AB* will not affect *CD,* but any sudden change in *AB* will communicate an impulse through the intervening particles and vortices, causing a reverse current in *CD,* which is then gradually dissipated by the resistance. This is induction. Quite unexpectedly the model also suggested a physical interpretation of the electrotonic function. In analyzing machinery several engineers, including Rankine, had found it useful to add to the motion of a mechanical part terms incorporating effects of connected gears and linkages, which they called the "reduced" inertia or momentum of the system. Maxwell discovered that the electrotonic function corresponds to the reduced momentum of the vortex system at each point. The equation for induced electromotive force $\mathbf{E} = \partial\mathbf{A}/\partial t$ is the generalized electrical equivalent of Newton's equation between force and rate of change of momentum.

There is good evidence internal and external to the paper that Maxwell meant originally to end here and did not begin Part 3 until Part 2 had been printed.[24] Meanwhile, he had been considering the relation between electric currents and the induction of charge through a dielectric. In 1854 he had remarked to Thomson that a literal treatment of the analogy between streamlines and lines of electric force would make induction nothing more than an extreme case of conduction.[25] Now, with the picture of electricity as disseminated in space, Maxwell hit upon a better description, based partly on Faraday's ideas, by making the vortex medium elastic. The forces between charged bodies could be attributed to potential energy stored in the medium by elastic distortion, as magnetic forces are attributed to stored rotational energy; and the difference between conduction and static electric induction is analogous to the difference between viscous and elastic processes in matter.

Two amazing consequences swiftly followed. First, since the electric particles surrounding a conductor are now capable of elastic displacement, a varying current is no longer entirely confined like water in a pipe: it penetrates to some extent into the space surrounding the wire. Here was the first glimmering of Maxwell's "displacement current." Second, any elastic substance with density ρ and shear modulus m can transmit transverse waves with velocity $v = \sqrt{m}/\rho$. Making some ad hoc assumptions about the elastic structure of the vortex medium, Maxwell derived while he was in Scotland formulas connecting ρ and m with electromagnetic quantities, which implied a numerical relationship between v and Weber's constant c. Returning to London for the academic year, Maxwell looked up the result of Kohlrausch and Weber's experiment to determine c, and after putting their data in a form suitable for insertion into his equation he found that for a medium having a magnetic permeability μ equal to unity v was almost equal to the velocity of light. With excitement manifested in italics he wrote: "we can scarcely avoid the inference that *light consists in the transverse undulations of the same medium which is the cause of electric and magnetic phenomena.*"[26] Thus the great discovery was made; and Maxwell, following a calculation on the dielectric properties of birefringent crystals, returned in Part 4 to his starting point, the magneto-optical effect, and replaced Thomson's spinning pendulum analogy with a more detailed theory in better accord with experiment.

In 1861 the British Association formed a committee under Thomson's chairmanship to determine a set of internationally acceptable electrical standards following the work of Weber. At Thomson's urging, a new absolute system of units was adopted, similar to Weber's, but based on energy principles rather than on a hypothetical electrodynamic force law. The first experiment was on the standard of resistance, and in 1862 Maxwell was appointed to the committee to help with that task. His third paper, "On the Elementary Relations of Electrical Quantities," written in 1863 with the assistance of Fleeming Jenkin, supplied a vital step in his development, often overlooked through its having been, most unfortunately, omitted from the *Scientific Papers*.[27] Extending a procedure begun by Fourier in the theory of heat, Maxwell set forth definitions of electric and magnetic quantities related to measures M, L, T of mass, length, and time, to provide the first—and one may also think the most lucid—exposition of that dual system of electrical units commonly but incorrectly known as the Gaussian system.[28] The paper introduced the notation, which was to become standard, expressing dimensional relations as products of powers of M, L, T enclosed in brackets, with separate dimensionless multipliers. For every quantity the ratio of the two absolute definitions, based on forces between electric charges and forces between magnetic poles, proved to be some power of a constant c with dimensions $[LT^{-1}]$ and magnitude $\sqrt{2}$ times Weber's constant, or very nearly the velocity of light. The analysis disclosed five different classes of experiments

100

from which c might be determined. One was a direct comparison of electrostatic and electromagnetic forces carried out by Maxwell and C. Hockin in 1868, and two others were started by Maxwell at Cambridge in the 1870's.[29] The results of many experiments over the next few years progressively converged with the measured velocity of light.

By 1863, then, Maxwell had found a link of a purely phenomenological kind between electromagnetic quantities and the velocity of light. His fourth paper, "A Dynamical Theory of the Electromagnetic Field," published in 1865, clinched matters. It provided a new theoretical framework for the subject, based on experiment and a few general dynamical principles, from which the propagation of electromagnetic waves through space followed without any special assumptions about molecular vortices or the forces between electric particles. This was the work of which Maxwell, in a rare moment of unveiled exuberance, wrote to his cousin Charles Cay, the mathematics master at Clifton College: "I have also a paper afloat, containing an electromagnetic theory of light, which, till I am convinced to the contrary, I hold to be great guns."[30]

Several factors, scientific and philosophical, settled the disposition of Maxwell's artillery. From the beginning he had stressed the provisional character of the vortex model, especially its peculiar gearing of

particles and vortices. Rankine was a cautionary
example. In an article on thermodynamics written
in 1877 Maxwell illuminated his own thought by
observing that the vortex theory of matter, which at
first served Rankine well, later became an encum-
brance, distracting his attention from the general
considerations on which thermodynamic formulas
properly rest.[31] Maxwell wished to avoid that trap.
Yet he did not abandon all the ground gained in 1862.
The idea of treating light and electromagnetism as
processes in a common medium remained sound.
Furthermore, the new theory was, as the title of the
paper stated, a dynamical one: the medium remained
subject to the general principles of dynamics. The
novelty consisted in deducing wave propagation from
equations related to electrical experiments instead
of from a detailed mechanism; that was why the
theory became known as the electromagnetic theory
of light. Again Sir William Hamilton's influence is
discernible. Maxwell's decision to replace the vortex
model of electromagnetic and optical processes by
an analysis of the relations between the two classes
of phenomena is a concretization of Hamilton's
doctrine of the relativity of knowledge: all human
knowledge is of relations between objects rather than
of objects in themselves.

More specifically the theory rested on three main
principles. Maxwell retained the idea that electric

and magnetic energy are disseminated, merely avoiding commitment to hypotheses about their mechanical forms in space. Here it is worth noticing that his formal expressions $\mathbf{B} \cdot \mathbf{H}/8\pi$ and $\mathbf{D} \cdot \mathbf{E}/8\pi$ for the two energy densities simply extend and interpret physically an integral transformation of Thomson's.[32] Next Maxwell revived various ideas about the geometry of lines of force from the 1856 paper. Third, and most important, he replaced the vortex hypothesis with a new macroscopic analogy between inductive circuits and coupled dynamical systems. The analogy seems to have germinated in Maxwell's mind in 1863, while he was working out the theory of the British Association resistance experiment.[33] In part it goes back to Thomson, especially to Thomson's use of energy principles in the theory of the electric telegraph.[34] It may be illustrated in various ways, of which the model shown in Figure 3, which Maxwell had constructed in 1874, is the most convenient.[35] Two wheels, P and Q, are geared together through a differential mechanism with adjustable flyweights. Rotations of P and Q represent currents in two circuits; the moments of inertia represent coefficients of induction; a frictional band attached to Q represents the resistance of the secondary circuit. Every feature of electromagnetic induction is seen here. So long as P rotates uniformly, Q remains stationary; but when P is started or stopped, a reverse impulse is trans-

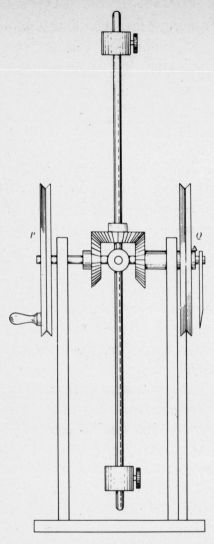

FIGURE 3. Dynamical analogy for two inductively coupled circuits (1865, 1874).

mitted to Q. This impulse is determined by the acceleration, the coefficient of coupling, and the inertia and resistance of Q, in exact analogy with an electrical system. Again the definitive quantity has the nature of momentum, determined in the mechanical model by the positions of the flyweights and in the electromagnetic analog by the geometry of the circuits. The total "electrokinetic momentum" $\mathbf{p}$ is $Li + \sum_j M_j i_j$, where L and i are the self-inductance and current in a particular circuit and the M_j's and i_j's are the mutual inductances and currents of neighboring circuits. Since $\mathbf{p}$ is the integral of the function $\mathbf{A}$ round the circuit, the analogy carries through at the macroscopic level Maxwell's identification of $\mathbf{A}$ with the "reduced momentum" of the field. Combined with conservation of energy, it also gives the mechanical actions between circuits. Helmholtz and Thomson had applied energy principles to deduce the law of induction from Ampère's force law; Maxwell inverted and generalized their argument to calculate forces from the induction formulas. Thus his first analytic treatment of the electrotonic function was metamorphosed into a complete dynamical theory of the field.

In the *Treatise* Maxwell extended the dynamical formalism by a more thoroughgoing application of Lagrange's equations than he had attempted in 1865. His doing so coincided with a general movement among British and European mathematicians about then toward wider use of the methods of analytical dynamics in physical problems. The course of that movement in Britain may be followed through Cayley's two British Association reports on advanced dynamics of 1857 and 1862, Routh's *Treatise on the Dynamics of a System of Rigid Bodies* (1860, 1868), and Thomson and Tait's *Treatise on Natural Philosophy* (first edition 1867). Maxwell helped Thomson and Tait with comments on many sections of their text. Then, with the freshness of outlook that makes his work so appealing, he turned the current fad to his own ends by applying it to electromagnetism. Using arguments extraordinarily modern in flavor about the symmetry and vector structure of the terms, he expressed the Lagrangian for an electromagnetic system in its most general form. Green and others had developed similar arguments in studying the dynamics of the luminiferous ether, but the use Maxwell made of Lagrangian techniques was new to the point of being almost a new approach to physical theory—though many years were to pass before other physicists fully exploited the ground he had broken. The beauty of the Lagrangian method is that it allows new terms to be incorporated in the theory automatically as they arise, with a minimum of physical hypothesis. One that Maxwell devoted a chapter of the *Treatise* to was the magneto-optical effect. By a

powerful application of symmetry considerations he
put Thomson's argument of 1856 on a rigorous basis
and proved that any dynamical explanation of the
rotation of the plane of polarized light must depend
on local rotation in the magnetic field. In later
terminology, the induction **B** is an axial vector, and
the electrons in matter precess about the applied
field: these are the elements of truth behind the molecular vortex hypothesis. Characteristically Maxwell
did not limit his thinking to the general symmetry
argument: he tested it by attempting to invent counter-
examples. Elsewhere he wrote, "I have also tried a
great many hypotheses [to explain the magneto-
optical effect] besides those which I have published,
and have been astonished at the way in which
conditions likely to produce rotation are exactly
neutralized by others not seen at first."[36] A further
instance of the power of the Lagrangian methods,
covered in the *Treatise*, is Maxwell's analysis of
cross-terms linking electrical and mechanical phenomena. This he did partly at the suggestion of
J. W. Strutt (Lord Rayleigh).[37] He identified three
possible electromechanical effects, later detected by
Barnett (1908), Einstein and de Haas (1916), and
Tolman and Stewart (1916). The Barnett effect is a
magnetic moment induced in a rapidly spinning iron
bar. Maxwell himself had looked for the inverse
phenomenon in 1861 during an experiment in search

107

of the angular momentum of molecular vortices.[38]

In 1865, and again in the *Treatise*, Maxwell's next step after completing the dynamical analogy was to develop a group of eight equations describing the electromagnetic field. They are set out in the table with subsidiary equations according to the form adopted in the *Treatise*. The principle they embody is that electromagnetic processes are transmitted by the separate and independent action of each charge (or magnetized body) on the surrounding space rather than by direct action at a distance. Formulas for the forces between moving charged bodies may indeed be derived from Maxwell's equations, but the action is not along the line joining them and can be reconciled with dynamical principles only by taking into account the exchange of momentum with the field.[39] Maxwell remarked that the equations might be condensed, but "to eliminate a quantity which expresses a useful idea would be rather a loss than a gain in this stage of our enquiry."[40] He had in fact simplified the equations in his fifth major paper, the short but important "Note on the Electromagnetic Theory of Light" (1868), writing them in an integral form without the function **A**, based on four postulates derived from electrical experiments. This may be called the electrical formulation of the theory, in contrast with the original dynamical formulation. It was later independently developed by Heaviside and Hertz and passed into the textbooks. It has the advantage of compactness and analytical symmetry, but its scope is more restricted and to some extent it concealed from the next generation of physicists ideas familiar to Maxwell which proved important later on. Two points in the table deserve comment for the modern reader. Equations (B) and (C) appear slightly unfamiliar, because (B) contains terms defined for a particular laboratory frame of reference, while (C), the so-called Lorentz force formula, contains a term in grad Ω for the force on isolated magnetic

General Equations of the Electromagnetic Field (1873)

A	Magnetic Induction	$\mathbf{B} = \text{curl } \mathbf{A}$
B	Electromotive Force	$\mathbf{E} = \mathbf{v} \wedge \mathbf{B} - \dot{\mathbf{A}} - \text{grad } \psi$
C	Mechanical Force	$\mathbf{F} = \mathbf{I} \wedge \mathbf{B} + e\mathbf{E} - m \text{ grad } \Omega$
D	Magnetization	$\mathbf{B} = \mathbf{H} + 4\pi\mathbf{J}$
E	Electric Currents	$4\pi\mathbf{I} = \text{curl } \mathbf{H}$
F	Current of Conduction	$\mathbf{I}' = C\mathbf{E}$
G	Electric Displacement	$\mathbf{D} = (1/4\pi) \mathbf{K}\mathbf{E}$
H	True Currents	$\mathbf{I} = \mathbf{I}' + \dot{\mathbf{D}}$
J	Induced Magnetization	$\mathbf{B} = \mu\mathbf{H}$
K	Electric Volume Density	$e = \text{div } \mathbf{D}$
L	Magnetic Volume Density	$m = \text{div } \mathbf{J}$

Note: Maxwell used $\mathbf{S}$ rather than $\mathbf{I}$ for electric current density.

poles, should such exist. Elsewhere in the *Treatise*[41] Maxwell began the investigation of moving frames of reference, a subject which in Einstein's hands was to revolutionize physics. The second point concerns the addition of the displacement current $\dot{\mathbf{D}}$ to the current of conduction $\mathbf{I}'$. In Maxwell's treatment (unlike later textbooks) the extra term appears almost without explanation, arising as it does from his analogy between the paired phenomena of conduction and static induction in electricity and viscous flow and elastic displacement in the theory of materials. More will be said later about the implications of Maxwell's view.

8. Electromagnetism: The Theory of Light and Critical Problems

Maxwell gave three distinct proofs of the existence of electromagnetic waves in 1865, 1868, and 1873. The disturbance has dual form, consisting in waves of magnetic force and electric displacement with motions perpendicular to the propagation vector and to each other. An alternative view given in the *Treatise* is to represent it as a transverse wave of the function **A**. In either version the theory yields strictly transverse motion, automatically eliminating the longitudinal waves which had embarrassed previous theories of light.

Among later developments, the generation and detection of radio waves by Hertz in 1888 stands supreme; but there were others of nearly comparable interest. In the *Treatise* Maxwell established that light, on the electromagnetic theory, exerts a radiation pressure. Radiation pressure had been the subject of much speculation since the early eighteenth century; before Maxwell most people had assumed that its existence would be a crucial argument in favor of a corpuscular rather than a wave theory of light. When

William Crookes discovered his radiometer effect in 1874, shortly after the publication of Maxwell's *Treatise*, some persons thought that he had observed radiation pressure, but the disturbance was much larger than the predicted value and in the wrong direction, and was caused, as will be explained below, by convection currents in the residual gas. Maxwell's formula was confirmed experimentally by Lebedev in 1900. The effect has implications in many branches of physics. It accounts for the repulsion of comets' tails by the sun; it is, as Boltzmann proved in 1884, critical to the theory of blackbody radiation; it may be used in deriving classically the time-dilation formula of special relativity; it fixes the mass-range of stars.

Another very fruitful new area of research started by Maxwell was on the connections between electrical and optical properties of bodies. He obtained expressions for the torque on a birefringent crystal suspended in an electric field, for the relation between refractive index and dielectric constant in transparent media, and for the relation between optical absorption and electrical conductivity in metals. In the long wavelength limit the refractive index may be expected on the simplest theory to be proportional to the square root of the dielectric constant. Measurements by Boltzmann, J. E. H. Gordon, J. Hopkinson, and others confirmed Maxwell's formula in gases and paraffin oils, but in some materials (most obviously, water) they revealed large discrepancies. These and like problems, including Maxwell's own observation of a discrepancy between the observed and predicted ratios of optical absorption to electrical conductivity in gold leaf, formed a basis for decades of research on electro-optical phenomena. Much of what was done during the 1880's and 1890's should be seen as the beginnings of modern research on solid-state physics, though a full interpretation waited on the development of the quantum theory of solids.

In classical optics Maxwell's theory worked a revolution that is now rarely perceived. A popular fiction among twentieth-century physicists is that mechanical theories of the ether were universally accepted and universally successful during the nineteenth century, until shaken by the null result of the Michelson-Morley experiment on the motion of the earth through the ether. This little piece of textbook folklore is wrong in both its positive and its negative assertions. More will be said below about the Michelson-Morley experiment, but long before that the classical ether theories were beset with grave difficulties on their own ground. The problem was to find a consistent dynamical foundation for the wave theory of light. During the 1820's Fresnel had given his well-known formulas for double refraction and for the reflection of polarized light; they were confirmed later with extraordinary experimental accuracy, but Fresnel's successors had immense trouble in reconciling them with each other on any mechanical theory of the ether. In 1862 Stokes summarized forty years of arduous research, during which a dozen different ethers had been tried and found wanting, by remarking that in his opinion the true dynamical theory of double refraction was yet to be found.[42] In 1865 Maxwell obtained Fresnel's wave surface for double refraction from the electromagnetic theory in the most straightforward way, completely avoiding the ad hoc supplementary conditions required in the mechanical theories. He did not then derive the reflection formulas, being uncertain about boundary conditions at high frequency;[43] but in 1874 H. A. Lorentz obtained them also very simply, using the static boundary condition Maxwell had given in 1856. An equivalent calculation, probably independent, appears in an undated manuscript of Maxwell's at Cambridge. The whole matter was investigated in two very powerful critical papers by Rayleigh (1881) and Gibbs (1888), and in the cycle of work begun by Thomson in his 1884 *Baltimore Lectures*. Rayleigh and Gibbs proved that Maxwell's were the only equations that give formulas for refraction, reflection, and scattering of light consistent with each other and with experiment.[44] Brief reference is appropriate here to James MacCullagh's semi-mechanical theory of 1845, in which the ether was assigned a property of rotational elasticity different from the elastic properties of any ordinary substance. After Stokes in 1862 had raised formidable objections against the stability of MacCullagh's medium, it was taken as disproved until FitzGerald and Larmor noticed a formal resemblance between MacCullagh's and Maxwell's equations. Since then the two theories have usually been considered homologous. In truth neither Stokes's objections to, nor Larmor's claims for, MacCullagh's theory can be sustained. A dynamically stable medium with rotational elasticity supplied by gyrostatic action was invented by Thomson in 1889.[45] On the other hand, whereas MacCullagh made kinetic energy essentially linear and elastic energy rotational, Maxwell identified magnetism with rotational kinetic energy and electrification with a linear elastic displacement. Very peculiar assumptions about the action of the ether on matter are necessary to carry MacCullagh's theory through at the molecular level; Maxwell's extends naturally and immediately to the ionic theory of matter. Even as an optical hypothesis, apart from its other virtues, the position of Maxwell's theory is unique.

Maxwell's statements about the luminiferous ether have an ambiguity which needs double care in view of the intellectual confusion of much twentieth-century comment on the subject. Selective quotation can make him sound as mechanistic as Thomson became in the 1880's or as Machian as Einstein was in the early 1900's. The *Treatise* concludes flatly that "there must be a medium or substance in which . . . energy exists after it leaves one body and before it reaches [an] other";[46] a later letter dismisses the ether as a "most conjectural scientific hypothesis."[47] Some remarks simply express the ultimate skepticism behind Maxwell's working faith in science. Others hinge on the view he inherited from Whewell that reality is ordered in a series of tiers, each more or less complete in itself, each built on the one below, and that the key to discovery lies in finding "appropriate ideas"[48] to describe the tier one is concerned with. By 1865 Maxwell was convinced that magnetic and electric energy are disseminated in space. As a "very probable hypothesis" he favored identifying the two forms of energy with "the motion and the strain of one and the same medium,"[49] but definite knowledge about one tier must be distinguished from reasonable speculation about the next. That was the philosophic point of the Lagrangian method. In Hamilton's terminology the best short statement of Maxwell's position is that we may believe in the existence of the ether without direct knowledge of its properties; we know only relations between the phenomena it accounts for. In a striking passage from the article on thermodynamics mentioned above, perhaps written after seeing the famous bells at Terling near Rayleigh's estate, Maxwell compared the situation to that of a group of bellringers confronted with ropes going to invisible machinery in the bell loft. Lagrange's equations supply the "appropriate idea" expressing neither more nor less than is known about the visible motions: whether more detailed information about the machinery can be gained later remains open. In Maxwell's, as in many later applications of Lagrange's method, the energies involve electrical, not mechanical, quantities. If the "very probable hypothesis" is followed out and one term is equated with ordinary kinetic energy, then, as Thomson found in 1855, a lower limit to the density ρ of a mechanical ether can be calculated from the known energy density of sunlight.[50] The flaw in Thomson's argument lies in assuming an energy density $\frac{1}{2}\rho v^2$; it is resolved in relativistic dynamics by the mass-energy relation; the rest mass of the photon is zero. Considerations of this kind indicate the subtlety of the scientific transformation wrought by relativity theory. It eliminated the arguments for an ether of fixed position and finite density, yet it preserved intact Maxwell's equations and his fundamental idea of disseminated electrical energy. More light is thrown on Maxwell's own opinions about the problem of relative and absolute motion and the connection between dynamics and other branches of physics by the delightful monograph *Matter and Motion,* published in 1877.

Maxwell's influence in suggesting the Michelson-Morley ether-drift experiment is widely acknowleged, but the story is a curiously tangled one. It originates in the problem of the aberration of starlight. During the course of a year the apparent positions of stars, as fixed by transit measurements, vary by ± 20.5 arc-seconds. This effect was discovered in 1728 by Bradley. He attributed it to the lateral motion of the telescope traveling at velocity v with the earth about the sun. On the corpuscular theory of light the motion causes a displacement of the image, while the particles travel from the objective to the focus, through an angular range v/c just equal to the observed displacement. An explanation of aberration on the wave theory of light is harder to come by. If the ether were a gas like the earth's atmosphere (as was first supposed), it would be carried along with the telescope and one scarcely would expect any displacement. Young in 1804 therefore proposed that the ether must pass between the atoms in the telescope wall "as freely perhaps as the wind passes through a grove of trees."[51] The idea had promise, but in working it out other phenomena needed to be considered, many of which further illustrate the difficulties of classical ethers. To explain Maxwell's involvement I depart from chronology and give the facts roughly in the order in which they presented themselves to him.

In 1859 Fizeau proved experimentally that the

velocity of light in a moving column of water is greater downstream than upstream. A natural supposition is that the water drags the ether along with it. This contradicts Young's hypothesis in its most primitive form; however, the modified velocity was not $c + w$ but $c + w(1 - 1/\mu^2)$, where μ is the refractive index of water, and that tallied with a more sophisticated theory of aberration due to Fresnel. Fresnel held the conviction (not actually verified until 1871) that the aberration coefficient in a telescope full of water must remain unchanged, which on Young's theory it does not. He was able to satisfy that requirement by combining Young's hypothesis with the further assumption that refraction is due to condensation of the ether in ordinary matter, the ether-density in a medium of refractive index μ being μ^2 times its value in free space. With the excess ether carried along by matter one obtains the quoted formula, which is in consequence still known as the "Fresnel drag" term, though it stands on broader foundations, as Larmor afterwards proved. Indeed Fresnel's condensation hypothesis is logically inconsistent with another principle that became accepted in the 1820's, namely, that the ether, to convey transverse but not longitudinal waves, must be an incompressible solid. A dissatisfaction with Fresnel's "startling assumptions" made Stokes in 1846 propose a radically new theory of aberration, treating the ether as a viscoelastic substance, like pitch or glass. For the rapid vibrations of light the ether acts as a solid, but for the slow motions of the solar system it resembles a viscous liquid, a portion of which is dragged along with each planetary body. A plausible circuital condition on the motion gives a deflection v/c for a beam of light approaching the earth, identical with the displacement that occurs inside the telescope in the other theories.

Some time in 1862 or 1863 Maxwell read Fizeau's paper and thought out an experiment to detect the ether wind. Since refraction is caused by differences in the velocity of light in different media, one might expect the Fresnel drag to modify the refraction of a glass prism moving through the ether. Maxwell calculated that the additional deflection in a 60° prism moving at the earth's velocity would be 17 arc-seconds. He arranged a train of three prisms with a return mirror behind them in the manner of his portable "colour-box," and set up what would now be called an autocollimator to look for the deflection, using a telescope with an illuminated eyepiece in which the image of the crosshair was refocused on itself after passing to and fro through the prisms. The displacement from ether motion could be seen by mounting the apparatus on a turntable, where the effect would reverse on rotating through 180°, giving an overall deflection after the double passage of $2\frac{1}{2}$ arc-minutes:

easily measurable. Maxwell could detect nothing, so in April 1864 he sent Stokes a paper for the Royal Society concluding that "the result of the experiment is decidedly negative to the hypothesis about the motion of the ether in the form stated here."[52]

Maxwell had blundered. Though he did not then know it, the French engineer Arago had done a crude version of the same experiment in 1810 (with errors too large for his result to have real significance), and Fresnel had based his theory on Arago's negative result. Stokes knew all this, having written an article on the subject in 1845; he replied, pointing out Maxwell's error, which had been to overlook the compensating change in density that occurs because the ether satisfies a continuity equation at the boundary.[53] Maxwell withdrew the paper. He did give a description of the experiment three years later, with a corrected interpretation, in a letter to the astronomer William Huggins, who included it in his pioneering paper of 1868 on the measurement of the radial velocities of stars from the Doppler shifts of their spectral lines.[54] There the matter rested until the last year of Maxwell's life. Then in his article "Ether" for the *Encyclopaedia Britannica* he again reviewed the problem of motion through the ether. The only possible earth-based experiment was to measure variations in the velocity of light on a double journey between two mirrors. Maxwell concluded that the time differences in different directions, being of the order v^2/c^2, would be too small to detect. He proposed another method from timing the eclipses of the moons of Jupiter, which he later described in more detail in a letter to the American astronomer D. P. Todd, published after his death in the Royal Society *Proceedings* and in *Nature*.[55] His statements there about the difficulties of the earth-based experiment served as a challenge to the young Albert Michelson, who at once invented his famous interferometer to do it.

The negative result of the experiment swung Michelson and everyone else behind Stokes's theory of aberration. In 1885, however, Lorentz discovered that Stokes's circuital condition on the motion of the ether is incompatible with having the ether stationary at the earth's surface. Lorentz advanced a new theory combining some of Stokes's ideas with some of Fresnel's; he also pointed out an oversight in Michelson's (and Maxwell's) analysis of the experiment, which halved the magnitude of the predicted effect, bringing it near the limits of the observations. Michelson and Morley then repeated the experiment with many improvements. Their conclusive results were published in 1887. In 1889 FitzGerald wrote to the American journal *Science* explaining the negative result by his contraction hypothesis.[56] The same idea was advanced independently by Lorentz in 1893. Physics texts often refer to the FitzGerald-Lorentz contraction as an ad hoc assumption dreamed up to save appearances. It was not. The force between two electric charges is a function of their motion with respect to a common frame: Maxwell had shown it (incompletely and in another context) in the *Treatise*.[57] Hence, as FitzGerald stated, all one need assume to explain the negative result of the Michelson-Morley experiment is that intermolecular forces obey the same laws as electromagnetic forces. The real (and great) merit of the special theory of relativity was pedagogical. It arranged the old confusing material in a clear deductive pattern.

Reference may be made to some more technical contributions from Maxwell's later work. A short paper of 1868, written after seeing an experiment by W. R. Grove, gave the first theoretical treatment of resonant alternating current circuits.[58] Portions of the *Treatise* applied quaternion formulas discovered by Tait to the field equations, and paved the way for Heaviside's and Gibbs's developments of vector analysis. Maxwell put these and various related matters in a wider context in a paper of 1870, "On the Mathematical Classification of Physical Quantities." He coined the terms "curl," "convergence" (negative divergence), and "gradient" for the various products of the vector operator ∇ on scalar and vector quantities, with the less familiar but instructive term "concentration" for the operation ∇^2, which gives the excess of a scalar V at a point over its average through the surrounding region.[59] He extended also his previous treatment of force and flux vectors, introduced the important distinction between what are now (after W. Voigt) known as axial and polar vectors, and in other papers gave a useful physical treatment of the two classes of tensors later distinguished mathematically as covariant and contravariant.[60] Further analytical developments in the *Treatise* include applications of reciprocal theorems to electrostatics, a general treatment of Green's functions, topological methods in field and network theory, and the beautiful polar representation of spherical harmonic functions.[61] The *Treatise* also contains important contributions to experimental technique, such as the well-known "Maxwell bridge" circuit for determining the magnitude of an inductance.[62]

A consequence of the displacement hypothesis which Maxwell himself did not truly grasp until 1869 is that all electric currents, even in apparently open circuits, are in reality closed.[63] But with that a new interpretation of electric charge became necessary. This is a subject of great difficulty, one of the most controversial in all Maxwell's writings. Many critics from Heinrich Hertz on have come to feel that a consistent view of the nature of charge and electric current, compatible with Maxwell's statements, simply does not exist. I believe these authors to be mistaken, although I admit that Maxwell gave them grounds for complaint, both by his laziness over plus and minus signs and by the fact that in parts of his work where the interpretation of charge was not the central issue he slipped back into terminology—and even ideas—not really compatible with his underlying view. The question is all the harder because the problem it touches (the relation between particles and fields) has continued as a difficulty in physics down to the present day. A full critical discussion would take many pages. I shall content myself with a short dogmatic statement, cautioning the reader that other opinions are possible.

Before Maxwell, electricity had been represented as an independent fluid (or pair of fluids), the excess or deficiency of which constitutes a charge. But if currents are invariably closed, how can charge accumulate anywhere? Part, but only part, of the answer lies in the hypothesis, hinted at by Faraday and clearly stated by Maxwell in 1865, that electrostatic action is entirely a matter of dielectric polarization, with the conductor serving not as a receptacle for electric fluid but as a bounding surface for unbalanced polarization of the surrounding medium. The difference between the old and new interpretations of charge, illustrated in Figure 4(a) and (b), looks simple;

125

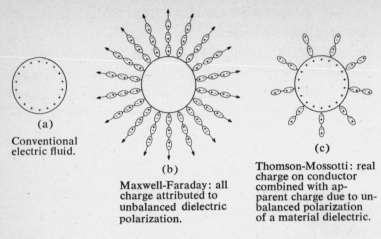

(a)

Conventional
electric fluid.

(b)

Maxwell-Faraday: all
charge attributed to
unbalanced dielectric
polarization.

(c)

Thomson-Mossotti: real
charge on conductor
combined with ap-
parent charge due to un-
balanced polarization
of a material dielectric.

FIGURE 4.   Representations of a charged conductor.

but underneath are problems that Maxwell's followers
found bafflingly obscure. One source of confusion
was that the polarization in 4(b) differs from that in
the theory of material dielectrics proposed earlier by
Thomson and Mossotti[64] (Figure 4[c]), which made
the effective charge Q at the boundary the sum of a
real charge Q_0 on the conductor and an apparent
charge $-Q'$ on the dielectric surface. In Maxwell's
interpretation the polarization extends from material
dielectrics to space itself; all charge is in a sense
apparent charge, and the motion is in the opposite
direction. All might have been well had Maxwell in
the *Treatise* not discussed the difference between
charge on a conductor and charge on a dielectric

surface in language similar to Mossotti's and if he had adopted a less liberal approach to the distinction between plus and minus signs. As it was, with the further novelty of totally closed currents, most people from Hertz on shook their heads in despair.

Yet the two analogies on which Maxwell based his ideas—those between the motion of electricity and an incompressible fluid and between static induction and displacement—are both sound. The escape lies in recognizing the radical difference in meaning of the two charges illustrated in 4(a) and 4(b). Maxwell's current is not the motion of charge, but the motion of a continuous *uncharged* quantity (not necessarily a substance); his charge is the measure of the displacement of that quantity relative to space. To the question puzzling Hertz—whether charge is the cause of polarization or polarization the cause of charge—the answer is "neither." For Maxwell electromotive force is the fundamental quantity. It causes polarization; polarization creates stresses in the field; charge is the measure of stress. All these ideas are traceable to Maxwell; but nowhere, it must be conceded, are they fairly set out. The representation of electricity as an uncharged fluid may seem incompatible with electron theory. Actually it is not; and one of the oddities in Maxwell's development is that the clue to reconciling the two ideas rests in the treatment of charges as sources and sinks of incompressible fluid given in his 1856 paper. That essentially was the principle of the ether-electron theory worked out by Larmor in 1899.

Few things illustrate better the subtlety of physical analogy than Maxwell's developing interpretations of the function A. His original discussion in 1856 was purely analytic. The dynamical theory led him to its representation as a property of electricity analogous to momentum, which reached fulfillment after his death in the expression $(mv + eA/c)$ for the canonical momentum of the electron, mv being the momentum of the free particle and eA/c the reduced momentum contributed by sources in the surrounding field. In 1871 he perceived another, entirely different analogy for A. Considered in relation to electro-dynamic forces it resembles a potential, as may be seen by comparing the equation $F = \text{grad}(i \cdot A)$ for force on a conductor carrying a current with the equation $F = \text{grad}(e\Phi)$ for force on a charged body. Maxwell introduced the terms "vector" and "scalar potential" for A and Φ and recognized, probably for the first time, that A was a generalization of F. E. Neumann's electrodynamic potential, though his formulation differed in spirit and substance from Neumann's, since it started from the field equations and incorporated displacement current. The formulas were later rearranged by FitzGerald, Liénard, and Wiechert as retarded potentials of the conduction

128

currents, thus uncovering their common ground with L. V. Lorenz's propagated action theory of electrodynamics. Both of Maxwell's analogies may be carried through in detail: that is, equations in **A** exist analogous to every equation in dynamics involving momentum and every equation in potential theory involving Φ. The resemblance of a single function to two quantities so different as momentum and potential depends on the peculiar relation between electromotive and electrodynamic forces: the electromotive force generated by induction is proportional to the velocity of the conductor times the electrodynamic force acting on it. The momentum analogy was little appreciated until 1959, when Y. Aharonov and D. J. Bohm pointed out some unexpected effects tied to the canonical momentum in quantum mechanics.[65]

A quality of Maxwell's work in electromagnetism, emphasized by Daniel M. Siegel in a short but illuminating article in *Isis,* is the "goal of completeness." At each stage Maxwell seeks a formulation that stays within existing knowledge yet leaves room for future advances. The possibility of adding new terms to the Lagrangian in the dynamical theory has already been discussed; Dr. Siegel uncovers a parallel stylistic aim elsewhere. Thus Maxwell's extraordinary conclusion that all electric currents are closed currents follows upon the physical ideas of the vortex model, but before then, in the 1856 paper,

Maxwell had deliberately restricted his investigation to closed currents, recognizing that none of the experiments gave information about isolated current elements. The idea that *all* currents are closed currents then completes (in a quite unforeseen way) Maxwell's first view of the subject. A more technical illustration of "completion" is Maxwell's analysis in the 1856 paper of the relation between electromagnetic induction (induction by a changing current) and magnetoelectric induction (induction by the motion of a conductor through the magnetic field). Their relation is a hard point in classical electrodynamics. Starting with the electronic function $\mathbf{A}$, Maxwell gets the formula $\mathbf{E} = - \partial\mathbf{A}/\partial t$, which describes electromagnetic induction, and then extends it to magnetoelectric induction by replacing the partial differential with a complete differential, that is, by adding terms equivalent to $\mathbf{v} \cdot \text{grad } \mathbf{A}$. The result is then (with certain assumptions) transformable into the term $\mathbf{v} \wedge \mathbf{B}$ found in equation (B) of the table on page 109.

The search for completeness, so defined, is part of the architectural quality of Maxwell's mind. It is equally characteristic of his work in the kinetic theory of gases: for example, in the grouping of the apparently distinct gaseous properties, viscosity, diffusion and heat conduction under the general category of transport phenomena.

9. Statistical and Molecular Physics

[1859-1879]

The problem of determining the motions of large numbers of colliding bodies came to Maxwell's attention while he was investigating Saturn's rings. He dismissed it then as hopelessly complicated; but in April 1859, as he was finishing his essay for publication, he chanced to read a new paper by Rudolf Clausius on the kinetic theory of gases, which convinced him otherwise and made him transfer his interest to gas theory.

The idea of attributing pressure in gases to the random impacts of molecules against the walls of the containing vessel had been suggested before. Prevailing opinion, however, still favored Newton's hypothesis of static repulsion between molecules or one of its variants, such as Rankine's vortex hypothesis. Maxwell had been taught the static theory of gases as a student at Edinburgh. Behind the victory of kinetic theory led by Clausius and Maxwell lay two distinct scientific advances: the doctrine of conservation of energy, and an accumulation of enough experimental information about gases to

shape a worthwhile theory. Many of the new discoveries from 1780 on, such as Dalton's law of partial
pressures, the law of equivalent volumes, and measurements on the failure of the ideal gas equation near
liquefaction, came as by-products of chemical
investigations. Two developments especially important
to Maxwell were Thomas Graham's long series of
experiments on diffusion, transpiration, and allied
phenomena, also begun as chemical researches, and
Stokes's analysis of gas viscosity, made in 1850 as part
of a study on the damping of pendulums for gravitational measurements. Maxwell had used Stokes's
data in treating the hypothesis of gaseous rings for
Saturn. Viscosity naturally became one of his first
subjects for calculation in kinetic theory; to his
astonishment the predicted coefficient was independent
of the pressure of the gas. The experiments of his wife
and himself between 1863 and 1865, which confirmed
this seeming paradox, fixed the success of the theory.

Clausius' work appeared in two papers of 1857
and 1858, each of which contained results important
to Maxwell. The first gave a greatly improved
derivation of the known formula connecting pressure
and volume in a system of moving molecules:

$$pV = \tfrac{1}{3}nm\overline{v^2}, \tag{7}$$

where m is the mass of a molecule, $\overline{v^2}$ its mean square velocity, and n the total number of molecules, from which, knowing the density at a given pressure, Clausius deduced (as others had done earlier) that the average speed must be several hundred meters per second. Another matter, whose full significance only became apparent after Maxwell's work, was the exchange of energy between the translational and rotational motions of molecules. Clausius guessed that the average energies associated with the two types of motion would settle down to a constant ratio σ, and from thermodynamical reasoning he derived an equation relating σ to the ratio γ of the two specific heats of a gas.

Clausius' second paper was written to counter a criticism by the Dutch meteorologist C. H. D. Buys-Ballott, who objected that gas molecules could never be going as fast as Clausius imagined, since the odor of a pungent gas takes minutes to permeate a room. Clausius replied that molecules of finite diameter must be repeatedly colliding and rebounding in new directions, and he deduced from statistical arguments that the probability W of a molecule's traveling a distance L without collision is

$$W = e^{-L/l}, \tag{8}$$

where l is a characteristic "mean free path." Assuming for convenience that all molecules have equal velocity, Clausius found

133

$$\frac{1}{l} = \frac{4}{3}\,\pi s^2 N, \tag{9}$$

where s is their diameter and N their number density. He could not determine the quantities explicitly but guessed that l/s might be about 1,000, from which l had to be a very small distance. Since by equation (8) only a minute fraction of molecules travel more than a few mean free paths without collision, Buys Ballot's objection to kinetic theory was fallacious.

Although Clausius had based his investigation on the simplifying assumption that all molecules of any one kind have the same velocity, he recognized that the velocities would in reality spread over a range of values. The first five propositions of Maxwell's "Illustrations of the Dynamical Theory of Gases" (1860) led to a statistical formula for the distribution of velocities in a gas at uniform pressure, as follows. Let the components of molecular velocity in three axes be x, y, z. Then the number dN of molecules whose velocities lie between x and $x + dx$, y and $y + dy$, z and $z + dz$ is $Nf(x)f(y)f(z)\,dx\,dy\,dz$. But since the axes are arbitrary, dN depends only on the molecular speed v, where $v^2 = x^2 + y^2 + z^2$ and the distribution must satisfy the functional relation

$$f(x)f(y)f(z) = \phi(x^2 + y^2 + z^2), \tag{10}$$

the solution of which is an exponential. Applying the

fact that N is finite, the resolved components of velocity in a given direction may be shown to have a distribution function identical in form with Laplace's bell-shaped "normal distribution" in the theory of errors:

$$dN_x = \frac{N}{\alpha \sqrt{\pi}} e^{-x^2/\alpha^2} dx, \tag{11}$$

where α is a quantity with dimensions of velocity. The number of particles summed over all directions with speeds between v and $v + dv$ is

$$dN_v = \frac{4N}{\alpha^3 \sqrt{\pi}} v^2 e^{-v^2/\alpha^2} dv. \tag{12}$$

Related formulas give the distributions in systems of two or more kinds of molecules. From them with (11) and (12) Maxwell was able to determine mean values of various products and powers of the velocities used in calculating gas properties.

The derivation of equations (11) and (12) marks the beginning of a new epoch in physics. Statistical methods had long been used for analyzing observations, both in physics and in the social sciences, but Maxwell's idea of describing actual physical processes by a statistical function was an extraordinary novelty. Its origin and validity deserve careful study. Intuitively equation (12) is plausible enough, since dN_v approaches zero as v approaches zero and infinity

135

and has a maximum at $v = \alpha$, consistent with the
natural physical expectation that only a few molecules
will have very high or very low speeds. Empirically
it was verified years later in experiments with molecular beams. Yet the assumption that the three
resolved components of velocity are distributed
independently is one which, as Maxwell later conceded, "may appear precarious";[66] and the whole
derivation conveys a strange impression of having
nothing to do with molecules or their collisions. Its
roots go back to Maxwell's Edinburgh days. His
interest in probability theory was aroused in 1848
by Forbes, who reexamined a statistical argument for
the existence of binary stars put forward in 1767 by
the Reverend John Michell. Over the next few years
he read thoroughly the statistical writings of Laplace
and Boole and also another item of peculiar interest,
a long essay by Sir John Herschel in the *Edinburgh
Review* for June 1850 on Adolphe Quetelet's *Theory
of Probability as Applied to the Moral and Social
Sciences*. Herschel's review ranged over many issues,
social and otherwise; and a contemporary letter to
Lewis Campbell leaves no doubt that Maxwell had
read it.[67] One passage embodied a popular derivation
of the law of least squares applied to random distributions in two dimensions, based on the supposed
independence of probabilities along different axes.
The family resemblance to Maxwell's derivation of

equation (11) is striking. Thus early reading on statistics, study of gaseous rings for Saturn, and ideas from Clausius about probability and free path all contributed to Maxwell's development of kinetic theory.

In his second paper, published in 1867, Maxwell offered a new derivation of the distribution law tied directly to molecular encounters. To maintain equilibrium the distribution function must satisfy the relation $f(v_1)f(v_2) = f(v_1')f(v_2')$ where v_1 and v_1' are velocities of molecule 1 and v_2 and v_2' of molecule 2 before and after encounter. Combination with the energy equation yielded formulas corresponding to (11) and (12). This established the equilibrium of the exponential distribution but not its uniqueness. From considerations of cyclic collision processes Maxwell sketched an argument that any velocity distribution would ultimately converge to the same form. The proof of the theorem in full mathematical rigor is still an open problem. Boltzmann gave an interesting extended version of Maxwell's argument in his *Lectures on Gas Theory* (1892). Earlier he had formulated another approach (the *H*-theorem), which bears on the subject and is even more important as part of the development that eventually transcended gas theory and led to the separate science of statistical mechanics. One further point that has been examined by various writers is the status of Maxwell's original derivation of the exponential law. Since the result is correct the hypotheses on which it was based must in some sense be justifiable. The best proof along Maxwell's first lines appears to be one given by M. Kac in 1939.[68]

Maxwell next applied the distribution function to evaluate coefficients of viscosity, diffusion, and heat conduction, as well as other properties of gases not studied by Clausius. He interpreted viscosity as the transfer of momentum between successive layers of molecules moving, like Saturn's rings, with different transverse velocities. The probability of a molecule's starting in a layer dz and ending in dz' is found from Clausius' equation (8) in combination with the distribution function. Integration gives the total frictional drag and an equation for the viscosity coefficient,

$$\mu = \tfrac{1}{3}\rho \bar{l}\bar{v}, \tag{13}$$

where ρ is the density, $\bar{l}$ the mean free path, and $\bar{v}$ the mean molecular speed. Since $\bar{l}$ is inversely proportional to ρ, the viscosity is independent of pressure. The physical explanation of this result, given by Maxwell in a letter to Stokes of 30 May 1859, is that although the number of molecules increases with pressure, the average distance over which each one carries momentum decreases with pressure.[69] It holds experimentally over a wide range, only breaking down when ρ is so high that $\bar{l}$ becomes comparable with the diameter of a molecule or so low that it is comparable with the dimensions of the apparatus. Maxwell was able to calculate a numerical value for the free path by substituting into (13) a value for μ/ρ from Stokes's data and a value for $\bar{v}$ from (7). The result was 5.6×10^{-6} cm. for air at atmospheric pressure and room temperature, which is within a factor of two of the current value. The calculations for diffusion and heat conduction proceeded along similar lines by determining the number of molecules and quantity of energy transferred in the gas. Applying the diffusion formulas to Graham's experiments, Maxwell made a second, independent estimate of the free path in air as 6.3×10^{-6} cm. The good agreement between the results greatly strengthened the plausibility of the theory. There were, however, errors of principle and of arithmetic in some of the calculations, which Clausius exposed—not without a certain scholarly relish—in a new paper of 1862. The chief mistake lay in continuing to use an isotropic distribution function in the presence of density and pressure gradients. Clausius offered a corrected theory; but since he persisted in assuming constant molecular velocity, it too was unsatisfactory. Maxwell wrote out his own revised theory in 1864; but having meanwhile become dissatisfied with the whole mean free path method, he withheld the details. The true value of Clausius' criticism was to show the need for a formulation of kinetic theory consistent with known macroscopic equations. Maxwell was to produce it in 1867.

One further important topic covered in the 1860 papers was the distribution of energy among different modes of motion of the molecules. Maxwell first established an equality, which had previously been somewhat sketchily derived by both Waterston and Clausius, between the average energies of translation of two sets of colliding particles with different molecular weights. He deduced that equal volumes of gas at fixed temperature and pressure contain the same number of molecules, accounting for the law of equivalent volumes in chemistry. Later, following out Clausius' thoughts on specific heat, he studied the distribution of energy between translational and rotational motions of rough spherical particles and found that there too the average energies are equal. These two statistical equalities, between the separate translational motions of different molecular species and between the rotational and translational motions of a single species, are examples of a deep general principle in statistical mechanics, the "equipartition principle." The second was an embarrassing surprise; for if molecules are point particles incapable of rotation, Clausius' formula makes the specific heat ratio 1.666, and if they are rough spheres it makes it 1.333. The experimental mean for several gases was 1.408. Maxwell was so upset that he stated that

140

the discrepancy "overturned the whole hypothesis."[70] His further wrestlings with equipartition in the 1870's will be discussed below.

The measurements of gaseous viscosity at different pressures and temperatures made by Maxwell and his wife[71] in 1865 were their most useful contribution to experimental physics. The "Dynamical Theory of Gases," which followed, was Maxwell's greatest single paper. The experiment consisted in observing the decay of oscillations of a stack of disks torsionally suspended in a sealed chamber. Over the ranges studied, the viscosity μ was independent of pressure, as predicted, and very nearly a linear function of the absolute temperature T. But equation (12) implies that μ should vary as $T^{1/2}$. The hypothesis that gas molecules are freely colliding spheres is therefore too simple, and Maxwell accordingly developed a new theory treating them as point centers of force subject to an inverse nth power repulsion. In a theory of this kind the mean free path ceases to be a clear-cut concept: molecules do not travel in straight lines but in complicated orbits with deflections and distances varying with velocity and initial path. Yet some quantity descriptive of the heterogeneous structure of the gas is needed. Maxwell replaced the characteristic distance l by a characteristic time, the "modulus of time of relaxation" of stresses in the gas. A second need, exposed by Clausius' critical paper of 1862, was for a systematic procedure to connect molecular motions with the known macroscopic gas laws. On both points Maxwell's thinking was influenced by Stokes's work on the general equations of viscosity and elasticity.

Elasticity may be defined as a stress developed in a body in reaction to change of form. Both solids and fluids exhibit elasticity of volume; solids alone are elastic against change of shape. A fluid resists changes of shape through its viscosity, but the resistance is evanescent: motion generates stresses proportional to velocity rather than displacement. In 1845 Stokes wrote a powerful paper giving a new treatment of the equations of motion of a viscous fluid. He noticed while doing so that if the time derivatives in the equations are replaced by spatial derivatives, they become the equations of stress for an elastic solid. Poisson also had noticed this transformation, but Stokes went further and remarked that viscosity and elasticity seem to be physically related through time. Substances like pitch and glass react as solids to rapid disturbances and as viscous liquids to slow ones. Stokes utilized this idea in the theory of aberration already described; other physicists also followed it up, among them Forbes, who, as an alpinist, applied it to the motions of glaciers. Maxwell's early letters contain several references to Forbes's opinions.[72] His youthful work on elasticity

142

made him acquainted with Stokes's paper, and in 1861, as explained above in the section on electricity, he applied the analogy of viscosity and elasticity in another way to the processes of conduction and static induction through dielectrics.

During the experiments on gases Maxwell's attention was again directed to viscoelastic phenomena through having to correct for losses in the torsion wire from which his apparatus was suspended. His 1867 paper proposed a new method of specifying viscosity in extension of Stokes's theory. In an ideal solid free from viscosity, a distortion or strain S of any kind creates a constant stress F equal to E times S, where E is the coefficient of elasticity for that particular kind of strain. In a viscous body F is not constant but tends to disappear. Maxwell conjectured that the rate of relaxation of stress is proportional to F, in which case the process may be described formally by the differential equation

$$\frac{dF}{dt} = E\frac{dS}{dt} - \frac{F}{\tau},\qquad(14)$$

which gives an exponential decay of stress governed by the relaxation time τ. Processes short compared with τ are elastic; processes of longer duration are viscous. The viscosity μ is equal to E_s times τ, where E_s is the instantaneous rigidity against shearing stresses. A given substance may depart from solidity

143

either by having small rigidity or short relaxation time, or both. Maxwell seems to have arrived at (14) from a comparison with Thomson's telegraphy equations, inverting the analogy between electrical and mechanical systems that he had developed in 1865. A test that immediately occurred to him was to look for induced double refraction in a moving fluid, comparable to the double refraction in strained solids discovered by Brewster, which he himself had analyzed in his paper of 1850 on the equilibrium of elastic solids. After some difficulty Maxwell eventually demonstrated in 1873 that a solution of Canada balsam in water exhibits temporary double refraction with a relaxation time of order 10^{-2} seconds.[73] Maxwell's theory of stress relaxation formed the starting point of the science of rheology and affected indirectly every branch of physics, as may be seen from the widespread use of his term "relaxation time." Its immediate purpose lay in reaching a new formulation of the kinetic theory of gases.

Consider a group of molecules moving about in a box. Their impact on the walls exerts pressure. If the volume is changed from V to $V + dV$, the pressure will change by an amount $-p\,dV/V$. But in the theory of elasticity the differential stress due to an isotropic change of volume is $-E\,dV/V$, where E is the cubical elasticity. The elasticity of a gas is proportional to its pressure. Suppose now the pressure

144

is reduced until the mean free path is much greater than the dimensions of the box; and let the walls be rough, so that the molecules rebound at random, and also flexible. Then in addition to the pressure there will be continued exchange of the transverse components of momentum from wall to wall, making the box, even though it is flexible, resist shearing stresses. In other words, a rarefied gas behaves like an elastic solid! Let this property be called quasi-solidity. Following the ideas expressed in equation (14), the viscosity of a gas at ordinary pressures may be conceived of as the relaxation of stresses by molecular encounters. Since elasticity varies as pressure, μ is proportional to $p\tau$ and the relaxation time of a gas at normal pressures is inversely proportional to its density. Although the concept of free path is elusive when there are forces between molecules, some link evidently exists between it and the relaxation time. Maxwell gave it in 1879 in a footnote to his last paper, added in response to a query by Thomson.[74] For a gas composed of rigid-elastic spheres, the product of τ with the mean speed $\bar{v}$ of the molecules is a characteristic distance λ, whose ratio to the mean free path $\bar{l}$ is $8/3\pi$. The free path is a special formulation of the relaxation concept applicable only to freely colliding particles of finite diameter.

To calculate the motions of a pair of molecules

subject to an inverse nth power repulsion was a straightforward exercise in orbital dynamics. For the statistical specification of encounters, Maxwell wrote the number dN, of molecules of a particular type with molecular weight M, and velocities between ξ_1 and $\xi_1 + d\xi$, etc. as $f(\xi_1 \eta_1 \zeta_1)\, d\xi_1\, d\eta_1\, d\zeta_1$, as in the first paper, with a similar expression for molecules of another type with molecular weight M_2. The velocities of two such groups being defined, their relative velocity V_{12} is also a definite quantity; and the number of encounters between them occurring in time δt can be expressed in terms of orbit parameters. It is $V_{12} b\, db\, d\phi\, dN_1\, dN_2\, \delta t$, where b is the distance between parallel asymptotes before and after an encounter and ϕ is the angle determining the plane in which V_{12} and b lie. If Q is some quantity describing the motion of molecules in group 1, which may be any power or product of powers of the velocities or their components, and if Q' is its value after an encounter, the net rate of change in the quantity for the entire group is $(Q' - Q)$ times the number of encounters per second, or

$$\frac{\delta}{\delta t}(Q\, dN_1) = (Q' - Q)\, V_{12} b\, db\, d\phi\, dN_1\, dN_2. \quad (15)$$

Equation (13) is the fundamental equation of Maxwell's revised transfer theory, replacing the earlier equations based on Clausius' probability formula (8).

With the explicit relation between V_{12} and b inserted from the orbit equation, the relative velocity enters the integral of (15) as a factor $V_{12}^{(n-5)/(n-1)}$, which means that although integration generally requires knowledge of the distribution function f_2 under nonequilibrium conditions, in the special case of molecules subject to an inverse fifth-power repulsion V_{12} drops out and the final result may be written immediately as $\bar{Q}N_2$, where $\bar{Q}$ is the mean value of the quantity and N_2 is the total number of molecules of type 2. The simplification may be understood, as Boltzmann later pointed out, by noticing that the number of deflections through a given angle is the product of two factors, one of which (the cross section for scattering) decreases with V_{12}, while the other (the number of collisions) increases with V_{12}.[75] When n is 5, the two factors are exactly balanced. Molecules subject to this law are now called Maxwellian. By a happy coincidence their viscosity is directly proportional to the absolute temperature, in agreement with Maxwell's experiment, although not with more precise measurements made later.

With this Maxwell was in a position to determine the scattering integrals and calculate physical properties of gases. Even with the simplification of inverse fifth-power forces the mathematical task remained formidable, and an impressive feature was the notation Maxwell developed to keep track of different problems. One general equation described transfer of quantities across a plane with different Q's giving the velocities, pressures, and heat fluxes in a gas. Next to be considered were variations of $\overline{Q}$ within a given element of volume. These might occur through the actions of encounters or external forces on molecules within the element or, alternatively, through the passage of molecules to or from the surrounding region. Denoting variations of the first kind by the symbol δ and variations of the second kind by ∂, Maxwell got his general equation of transfer:

$$\frac{\partial}{\partial t}\,\overline{Q}N + \left(\frac{du}{dx} + \frac{dv}{dy} + \frac{dw}{dz}\right) + \frac{d}{dx}\,(\overline{\xi Q}N)$$

$$+ \frac{d}{dy}\,(\overline{\eta Q}N) + \frac{d}{dz}\,(\overline{\zeta Q}N) = \frac{\delta}{\delta t}\,QN, \quad (16)$$

where u, v, w are components of the translational velocity of the gas; the differential symbol d gives total variations with respect to position and time; and subscripts are added to δ, to distinguish variations due to encounters with molecules of the same kind, molecules of a different kind, and the action of external forces. With Q equal to mass, (16) reduces to the ordinary equation of continuity in hydrodynamics. With Q equal to the momentum per unit volume, (16) in combination with the appropriate expression for

$\dfrac{\delta}{\delta t}\,QN$ derived from (15) reduces to an equation of motion. From this, or rather from its generalization to mixtures of more than one kind of molecule, Maxwell derived Dalton's law of partial pressures, and formulas for diffusion applicable to Graham's experiments. With Q energy, (16) yields an equation giving the law of equivalent volumes and formulas for specific heats, thermal effects of diffusion, and coefficients of viscosity in simple and mixed gases. The viscosity equation replacing (12) for Maxwellian molecules is

$$\mu = 0.3416k \left(\frac{M}{K}\right)^{\frac{1}{2}} T, \qquad (17)$$

where k is Boltzmann's constant, M is molecular weight, and K is the scaling constant for the forces.

The hardest area of investigation was heat conduction. That was where Maxwell had gone astray in 1860. In the exact theory effects of thermal gradients occur when Q in equation (16) is of the third order in ξ, η, ζ. Maxwell found an expression for the thermal conductivity of a gas in terms of its viscosity, density, and specific heat. The ratio of these quantities, which is known as the Prandtl number, "but which ought to be called the Maxwell number,"[76] is one of several dimensionless ratios used in applying similarity principles to the solution of problems in fluid dynamics. For a monatomic gas it is nearly a constant over a wide range of temperatures and pressures.

149

Another matter, in which Maxwell became interested through considering the stability of the earth's atmosphere, was the equilibrium of temperature in a vertical column of gas under gravity. The correct result was known from thermodynamics, but its derivation from gas theory gave Maxwell great trouble. It comes out right only if the ratio of the two statistical averages $\overline{\xi^4}/|\overline{\xi^2}|^2$ has the particular value 3 given by the exponential distribution law. The calculation thus supplied evidence in favor of the law. More light on the same subject came in Boltzmann's first paper on kinetic theory, written in 1868. Boltzmann investigated the distribution law by a method based on Maxwell's, but included the external forces directly in the energy equation to be combined with Maxwell's collision equation $f(v_1)f(v_2) = f(v_1')f(v_2')$. The distribution function assumed the form $e^{-E/kT}$, where E is the sum of the kinetic and potential energies of the molecule. In 1873 Maxwell gave a greatly simplified derivation of Boltzmann's result during a correspondence in *Nature* about the equilibrium of the atmosphere. He then confessed that his first calculation for the 1867 paper, which gave a temperature distribution that would have generated unending convection currents, nearly shattered his faith in kinetic theory.

Maxwell never attempted to solve the transfer equations for forces other than the inverse fifth power.

In 1872 Boltzmann rearranged (16) into an integro-differential equation for f, from which the transport coefficients could in principle be calculated; but despite much effort he failed to reach any solution except for Maxwellian molecules. It was not until 1911–1917 that S. Chapman and D. Enskog developed general methods of determining the coefficients. One interesting result was Chapman's expression for viscosity of a gas made up of hard spheres, which had a form equivalent to (12) but with a numerical coefficient 50 percent higher than Maxwell's and 12 percent higher than that obtained from the mean free path method with corrections for statistical averaging and persistence of velocities derived by Tait and Jeans. So even for the hard-sphere gas the simple theory fails in quantitative accuracy.

For some years after 1867 Maxwell made only sporadic contributions to gas theory. In 1873 he gave a revised theory of diffusion for the hard-sphere gas, from which he developed estimates of the size of molecules, following the work of Loschmidt (1865), Johnstone Stoney (1868), and Thomson (1870). In 1875, following van der Waals, he applied calculations on intermolecular forces to the problem of continuity between the liquid and gaseous states of matter. In 1876 he gave a new theory of capillarity, also based on considerations about intermolecular forces, which stimulated new research on surface phenomena.

Of all the questions about molecules which Maxwell puzzled over during this period the most urgent concerned their structure. His uneasiness about the discrepancy between the measured and calculated specific heat ratios of gases has already been referred to. The uneasiness increased after 1868 when Boltzmann extended the equipartition theorem to every degree of freedom in a dynamical system composed of material particles; and it turned to alarm with the emergence of a new area of research: spectrum analysis. From 1858 onwards, following the experiments of Bunsen and Kirchhoff, several people, including Maxwell, worked out a qualitative explanation of the bright lines in chemical spectra, attributing them to resonant vibrations of molecules excited by their mutual collisions. The broad truth of the hypothesis seemed certain; but it led, as Maxwell immediately saw, to two questions, neither of which was answered until after his death. First, the identity of spectra implies that an atom in Sirius and an atom in Arcturus must be identical in all the details of their internal structure. There must be some universal dimensional constant determining vibration frequency: "each molecule . . . throughout the universe bears impressed on it the stamp of a metric system as distinctly as does the metre of the Archives of Paris, or the double royal cubit of the Temple of Karnac."[77] The royal cubit proved to be

Planck's quantum of action discovered in 1900. The other question, also answered only by quantum theory, concerned the influence of molecular vibrations on the specific heat ratio. There were not three or six degrees of freedom, but dozens. There was no way of reconciling the specific heat and spectroscopic data with each other and the equipartition principle. The more Maxwell examined the problem the more baffled he became. In his last discussion, written in 1877, after summarizing and rejecting all the attempts from Boltzmann on to wriggle out of the difficulty, he concluded that nothing remained but to adopt that attitude of "thoroughly conscious ignorance that is the prelude to every real advance in knowledge."[78]

During his last two years Maxwell returned to molecular physics in earnest and produced two full-length papers, strikingly different in scope, each among the most powerful he ever wrote. The first, "On Boltzmann's Theorem on the Average Distribution of Energy in a System of Material Points," followed a line of thought started by Boltzmann, who in 1868 had offered a new conjectural derivation of the distribution law based on combinatorial theory. A strange feature of the analysis was that it seemed to be free from restrictions on the time spent in encounters between molecules. Hence, as Maxwell was quick to point out,[79] both the distribution factor $e^{-E/kT}$ and the equipartition theorem should apply to

153

solids and liquids as well as gases: a conclusion as fascinating and disturbing as equipartition itself.

Maxwell now gave his own investigation of the statistical problem, based partly on Boltzmann's ideas and partly on an extension of them contained in H. W. Watson's *Treatise on the Kinetic Theory of Gases.*[80] Following Watson, Maxwell used Hamilton's form of the dynamical equations, and adopted the device of representing the state of motion of a large number n of particles by the location of a single point in a "phase-space" of $2n$ dimensions, the coordinates of which are the positions and momenta of the particles. Boltzmann had applied similar methods in configuration space, but the Hamiltonian formalism has advantages in simplicity and elegance. Maxwell then postulated, as Boltzmann had done, that the system would in the course of time pass through every phase of motion consistent with the energy equation. This postulate obviously breaks down in special instances, of which Maxwell gave some examples, but he argued that it should hold approximately for large numbers of particles, where discontinuous jumps due to collisions make the particles jog off one smooth trajectory to another. The validity of this hypothesis, sometimes called the ergodic hypothesis, was afterwards much discussed, often with considerable misrepresentation of Maxwell's opinions. Maxwell next introduced a new formal device for handling the statistical averages. In place of the actual system of particles under study, many similar systems are conceived to exist simultaneously, with identical energies but different initial conditions. The statistical problem is then transformed into determining the number of systems in a given state at any instant, rather than the development in time of a single system. The method had in some degree been foreshadowed by Boltzmann in 1872. It was later very greatly extended by Gibbs, following whom it is known as the method of "ensemble averaging." Maxwell's main conclusion was that the validity of the distribution and equipartition laws in a system of material particles is not restricted to binary encounters. An important result of a more technical kind was an exact calculation of the microcanonical density of the gas, with an expression for its asymptotic form as the number n of degrees of freedom in the system goes to infinity, while the ratio E/n is held constant. According to C. Truesdell, although the hypotheses on which the theorem was based were rather special, "no better proof was given until the work of Darwin and Fowler."[76] Together with Boltzmann's articles this paper of Maxwell's marks the emergence of statistical mechanics as an independent science.

One feature of the paper "On Boltzmann's Theorem," eminently characteristic of Maxwell, is that the analysis, for all its abstraction, ends with a concrete suggestion for an experiment, based on considering the rotational degrees of freedom. Maxwell proved that the densities of the constituent components in a rotating mixture of gases would be the same as if each gas were present by itself. Hence gaseous mixtures could be separated by means of a centrifuge. The method also promised much more accurate diffusion data than was hitherto available. Maxwell's correspondence before his death discloses a plan to set up experiments at Cambridge.[81] Many years later it became a standard technique for separating gases commercially.

Maxwell's last major paper on any subject was "On Stresses in Rarefied Gases Arising From Inequalities of Temperature." Between 1873 and 1876 the scientific world had been stirred by William Crookes's experiments with the radiometer, the well-known device composed of a partially evacuated chamber containing a paddle wheel with vanes blackened on one side and silvered on the other, which spins rapidly when radiant heat impinges on it. At first many people, Maxwell included, were tempted to ascribe the motion to light pressure, but the forces were much greater than predicted from the electro-magnetic theory, and in the wrong direction. The influence of the residual gas was soon established; and from 1874 on partial explanations were advanced by Osborne Reynolds, Johnstone Stoney, and others. The tenor of these explanations was that the blackened surfaces absorb radiation and, being hot, make the gas molecules rebound with higher average velocity than do the reflecting surfaces. That plausible but false notion is still perpetuated in many textbooks. A striking observation is that the stresses increase as the pressure is reduced. In 1875 Tait and James Dewar drew the significant conclusion that large stresses occur when the mean free path is comparable with the dimensions of the vanes. At higher pressures some equalizing process enters to reduce the effect.

Such was the state of affairs in 1877, when Maxwell and Reynolds independently renewed the attack. Maxwell was thoroughly familiar with the radiometer controversy, having acted as a referee for many of the original papers, as well as seeing and experimenting with radiometers himself.

Indeed he had demonstrated radiometers in the most exalted circles, as he explained to his uncle R. D. Cay in a letter of 15 May 1876, now preserved at Peterhouse, Cambridge:

I was sent for to London, to be ready to explain to the Queen why Otto von Guericke devoted himself to the discovery of nothing, and to show her the two hemispheres in which he kept it, and the pictures of the 16 horses who could not separate the hemispheres, and how after 200 years W. Crookes has come much nearer to nothing and has sealed it up in a glass globe for public inspection. Her Majesty however let us off very easily and did not make much ado about nothing, as she had much heavy work cut out for her all the rest of the day . . . .

Maxwell's analysis of the radiometer effect went forward in several stages, during which the comments of Thomson, who refereed his paper, and his own reaction as a referee for Reynolds' paper had important influences. He began by applying the exact transfer theory to the hypothesis that the stresses arise from the increased velocity of the molecules rebounding from a heated surface, expanding the distribution function in the form

$$[1 + F(\xi, \eta, \zeta)] \, e^{-(\xi^2 + \eta^2 + \zeta^2)/kT}, \qquad (18)$$

where F is a sum of powers and products of ξ, η, ζ up to the third degree, and then calculating the effect of temperature gradients in the gas. This expansion later became the first step of Chapman's elaborate procedure for determining transport coefficients under any force law, but Maxwell kept to inverse fifth-power forces "for the sake of being able to effect the integrations."[82] The result was a stress proportional to d^2T/dn^2, the second derivative of temperature with respect to distance, correcting a formula given earlier by Stoney, where the stress was proportional to dT/dn. The stress increases when the pressure is lowered, reaching a maximum when the relaxation time τ becomes comparable with the time $d/\bar{v}$, in which a molecule traverses the dimension d of the body—that is, Tait and Dewar's conjecture in the language of the exact theory.

At this point Maxwell made an awkward discovery. Although the stresses are indeed large, when the flow of heat is uniform (as in the radiometer) they automatically distribute themselves in such a way that the forces on each element of gas are in equilibrium. The result is a very general consequence of the fact that the stresses depend on d^2T/dn^2; it is almost independent of the shape of the source; the straightforward explanation of the motions by normal stresses must, therefore, be rejected. Yet the radiometer moves. To escape the dilemma, Maxwell turned to tangential stresses at the edges of the vanes. Here the phenomenon known as "slip" proved all-important. When a viscous fluid moves past a solid body, it generates tangential stresses by sliding over the surface with a finite velocity v_s. According to experiments by Kundt and Warburg in 1875, v_s in gases is equal to SG/μ, where S is the stress and G is a coefficient expressed empirically by $G = 8/\rho$. Thus slip effects increase as the pressure is reduced; and as Maxwell pointed out in 1878,[83] convection currents due to tangential stresses should become dominant in the radiometer, completely destroying the simplicity of the original hypothesis.

The second phase of Maxwell's investigation followed a report by Thomson urging him to treat the gas–surface interaction, and his own report on Reynolds' paper. Reynolds also had decided that the effect must depend on tangential stresses, and he devised an experiment to study them under simplified conditions. When a temperature difference ΔT is set up across a porous plug between two vessels containing gas at pressure p, a pressure difference Δp develops between them proportional to $\Delta T/p$. Reynolds called this new effect "thermal transpiration." Maxwell gave a simple qualitative explanation in his report, and in an appendix added to his own paper in May 1879 he developed a semiempirical theory accounting for it and for the radiometer effect. The method was to assume that a fraction f of molecules striking any surface are temporarily absorbed and reemitted diffusely, while the remaining $(1 - f)$ are specularly reflected. Application of the transfer equations gave a formula for the velocity v_s of gas moving past an unequally heated surface, in which one term was the standard slip formula and two further terms predicted convection currents due to thermal gradients. The theory provided an explicit expression $\frac{2}{3}(2/f - 1)\bar{l}$ for the coefficient G, where $\bar{l}$ is the effective mean

160

free path; from this, using Kundt and Warburg's data, Maxwell deduced that f is about 0.5 for air in contact with glass. Maxwell also obtained a formula for transpiration pressure, and showed that both radiometer and transpiration effects are in the correct direction and increase with reduction of pressure, in agreement with experiment.

Maxwell's paper created the science of rarefied gas dynamics. His formulas for stress and heat flux in the body of the gas were contributions of permanent value, while his investigation of surface effects started a vast body of research extending to the present day. Quantities similar to f later became known as "accommodation coefficients" and were applied to many kinds of gas–surface interaction. One other contribution of great beauty contained in notes added to the paper in May and June 1879 was an application of the methods of spherical harmonic analysis to gas theory. It exemplified the process which Maxwell elsewhere called the "cross-fertilization of the sciences."[84] He was engaged in revising the chapter on spherical harmonics for the second edition of the *Treatise on Electricity and Magnetism*, when he realized that the harmonic expansion used in potential theory could equally be applied to the expansion of the components ξ, η, ζ of molecular velocity. A standard theorem on products of surface and zonal harmonics, which is discussed in the *Treatise*, eliminates odd terms in the expansion of variations of F, greatly simplifying the calculations.[85] With this and other simplifications Maxwell carried the approximations to higher order and added an extra term to the equation of motion of a gas subject to variations in temperature.

It is a tribute to Maxwell's genius that on two occasions his papers on transfer theory stimulated fresh work long after the period at which science usually receives historical embalming. In 1910 Chapman read them, and "with the ignorant hardihood of youth,"[86] knowing nothing of the fruitless toil that had been spent on the equations during the interval, began his investigation that yielded solutions under any force law. In 1956 E. Ikenberry and C. Truesdell again returned to Maxwell. They obtained an exact representation formula for the collision integral of any spherical harmonic for inverse-fifth-power molecules, using which they explored various iterative techniques for solving the transfer equations. One technique, which they called "Maxwellian iteration" from its resemblance to Maxwell's procedure in the 1879 paper, yielded much more compact derivations than the Chapman-Enskog procedure; and with it Ikenberry and Truesdell carried solutions for pressure and energy flux in the gas one stage further than had previously been attempted. Truesdell also discovered an exact solution for steady rectilinear flow, by means of which he exposed certain shortcomings of the iterative methods. Speaking of the "magnificent genius of Maxwell" these authors concluded their appraisal by remarking that it passed over all developments in kinetic theory since 1879 and went back "for its source and inspiration to what Maxwell left us."[87]

10. Contributions to Other Scientific Fields

Maxwell's remaining work may be summarized more briefly, but it should not be regarded as being of small account. His early discovery of the perfect imaging properties of the "fish-eye" lens extended to a lifelong interest in the laws of optical instruments. In a medium whose refractive index varies as $\mu_0 a^2/(a^2 + r^2)$, where μ_0 and a are constants and r is the distance from the origin, all rays proceeding from any single point are focused exactly at another point. The calculation was "suggested by the contemplation of the structure of the crystalline lens in fish."[88] Real fishes' eyes of course only approximate roughly to Maxwell's medium. Not until R. K. Luneberg revived the subject in 1944 were other instances of perfect imaging devices found.[89] In 1853, shortly after discovering the "fish-eye," Maxwell came across the early-eighteenth-century writings on geometrical optics by Roger Cotes and Archibald Smith, in which, as he said to his father, "I find many things far better than what is new."[90] In 1856, making use of Cotes' neglected theorem on "apparent distance," he formulated a new approach to the subject, reducing the theory of a hypothetically perfect optical instrument to geometrical relations between points in the object and image spaces, without reference to lens systems. Previous investigators, even Gauss, had failed to separate the geometry from the dioptrics. An important particular result was Maxwell's elongation formula $M_L = (n'/n) M_T^2$, which relates the longitudinal magnification M_L of an image to its transverse magnification M_T and the ratio n'/n of the refractive indexes in the spaces. Maxwell was asked by the publisher Daniel Macmillan to do a monograph on geometrical optics; he wrote a considerable portion but dropped the task after leaving Cambridge for Aberdeen. In 1872, without any knowledge of Maxwell's work, Ernst Abbé developed the standard geometrical theory of images that bears his name. Recent years have seen a revival of interest in the special features of Maxwell's method.[91]

In 1867 Maxwell wrote a paper, "On the Cyclide," developing the geometry of wave surfaces near the foci of an astigmatic lens. This investigation is interesting not only for its elegant mathematics and for the beautiful stereoscopic views given by Maxwell of different classes of cyclides, but also because it illustrates how a study of terminology may throw light on the history of science. In the *Oxford English Dictionary* "cyclide" is defined as "the envelope of a sphere moving on a fixed quadric, and which cuts a fixed sphere orthogonally." The definition is taken from George Salmon's *Analytical Geometry of Three Dimensions,* 3rd ed., 1874: the earliest use cited by the OED and seven years later than Maxwell's paper. The first two editions of Salmon's work, dated 1862 and 1865, do not mention the cyclide. Salmon based his investigation on correspondence with Arthur Cayley and John Casey and on two original papers, one of 1869 by J. G. Darboux and another by Casey, "On Cyclides and Sphero-quartics," dated 1871: both also later than Maxwell. Casey cites Darboux, and also a paper by T. F. Moutard where the cyclide is called an anallagmatic surface, a term adopted also by Salmon in one special context. Maxwell, as usual, gives the historical answer in his paper. He refers his knowledge of the cyclide to P. C. F. Dupin's *Applications de Géometrie et de Mécanique des Arts et Métiers,* published in Brussels in 1825. The four forms of cyclides studied by Dupin and Maxwell were of a more restricted kind than those developed by Darboux, Casey, and Salmon, belonging to the group Salmon called tetranodal cyclides. Dupin originally defined the cyclide as the envelope of certain spheres that touch three fixed spheres in a continuous manner, choosing the name cyclide, as Maxwell remarks, "because both series of its lines of curvature are circles." Alternative definitions of Dupin's cyclide are discussed by Salmon, along with its relation to the more general surfaces. Maxwell's development of the theory seems to have been the first of any importance after Dupin's. Though ignored by the mathematicians, it contained several new themes, including inversion of cyclides, properties of confocal cyclides, and the formation of conjugate isothermal functions on cyclidal surfaces. Besides the application of advanced geometry to optics, Maxwell's paper has a special interest as containing a description of his clever "real image stereoscope."

In 1874 Maxwell again took up geometrical optics after becoming acquainted, through Tait, with Hamilton's idea of the "characteristic function." Hamilton had formed a method for investigating the properties of optical systems at distances arbitrarily far from the optic axis by the use of a certain function V of six variables, which gives in effect the time for a ray of light to pass between a point in the object space and one in the image space. Hamilton worked out an elaborate general theory involving V and three derived functions; he applied the method to several lens systems but left most of the practical applications in manuscript where they remained unknown until his papers were edited by A. W. Conway and J. L. Synge in 1930. Hamilton's method is difficult and no one else touched it until Maxwell. He wrote three papers in 1874 and 1875, in one of which he treated the theory of an axially symmetric instrument at some length and obtained the characteristic function V for a spherical surface correct to terms of the fourth order.

Later events illustrate the unpleasing phenomenon of scientific nationalism. In 1887 R. S. Heath wrote a large treatise on geometrical optics systematically extending the results of Hamilton and Maxwell. In 1895 H. Bruns, who apparently knew nothing of the British work, rediscovered the underlying idea of Hamilton's function, which he presented in a less general but somewhat easier form, calling it the "eikonal," or imaging, function, from the same root as the word icon. Thereafter historical facts adjusted themselves along with Anglo-German-Irish diplomacy. The contributors to the classic German treatise *Die Theorie der Optischen Instrumente* edited by M. von Rohr in 1903 wrote in the best tradition of German scholarship, judicious, indeed generous, in their assessment of Hamilton, Maxwell, and Heath, and passing lightly over Bruns. This work was translated into English in 1920. After the First World War other Germans claimed that Hamilton's method was impractical; it had never been developed; all the really important discoveries had followed from Bruns. The method then generally became known as the eikonal method. A historic polemic was conducted between J. L. Synge and

M. Herzberger in the *Journal of the Optical Society of America* during 1936 and 1937. The Irishman was then so obsessed with the wrongs done to his countryman that he swallowed the post-war German myth that Hamilton's seed had fallen on barren ground, apparently unaware of the writings of Maxwell and Heath. The ex-German made one reference to Maxwell but none to Heath.

The most pleasing of Maxwell's minor inventions was the adjustable "dynamical top" (1856), which carried a disk with four quadrants (red, blue, green, yellow) that formed gray when spinning axially "but burst into brilliant colours when the axis is disturbed." Through his study of the dynamics of rotation Maxwell was led to search the records at Greenwich for evidence of the earth's 10-month nutation predicted by Euler. Eventually S. C. Chandler in 1891 detected a 14-month nutation.

During his regular lectures at King's College, London, Maxwell was accustomed to present some of Rankine's work on the calculation of stresses in frameworks. In 1864 Rankine offered an important new theorem,[92] which Maxwell then developed into a geometrical discussion entitled "On Reciprocal Figures and Diagrams of Forces." The principle was an extension of the well-known triangle of forces in statics. Corresponding to any rectilinear figure, another figure may be drawn with lines parallel to the first, but arranged so that lines converging to a point in one figure form closed polygons in the other. The lengths of lines in the polygon supply the ratios of forces needed to maintain the original point in equilibrium. Maxwell gave a method for developing complex figures systematically, and derived a series of general theorems on properties of reciprocal figures in two or three dimensions, combining the method with energy principles. One result concerned the number of bars or lines needed to construct a stable figure joining a given number of points in space. Maxwell found that in general $(3n - 6)$ lines are needed for a figure of n points, but there are exceptions. Some striking examples invented in recent years are R. Buckminster Fuller's beautifully conceived if barbarically named "tensegrity spheres," the simplest of which consists of six intersecting pentagons having the corners of each pentagon joined to the midpoint of the next. The figure joins 30 points; each side of every pentagon, being centered on a point, counts as two lines, making 60 lines, 24 less than required by the Maxwell condition. Maxwell's original statement of his theorem embodies exactly the necessary qualification to cover such anomalous figures: "In those cases in which stiffness can be produced with a smaller number of lines, certain conditions must be fulfilled, rendering the case one of a maximum or minimum of one or more of

170

its lines. The stiffness of such frames is of an inferior order, as a small disturbing force may produce a displacement infinite in comparison with itself." The lines for the tensegrity sphere are all of the minimum length needed to complete the figure. The pairing of the 60 lines into 30 stiff bars of finite thickness adds enough torsional rigidity to the real figure to compensate for the "inferior order" of stiffness of the ideal figure on which the theory is based. The final structure has a delightful airy elegance.

In 1870, after refereeing a paper on elasticity by G. B. Airy, Maxwell extended the method of reciprocal functions to continuous media in a brilliant essay to which the Royal Society of Edinburgh awarded its Keith medal.[93] Figure 5 reproduces the diagram of a girder bridge and its reciprocal supplied by Fleeming Jenkin for that paper. In 1873 R. H. Bow invented a clever notation to simplify the process of drawing the figures. The method of reciprocal diagrams was developed in Germany by K. Culmann, in France by M. Lévy, and in Italy by G. Cremona, amid further national claims and counterclaims. On a larger scale the subject forms part of the wide development after 1810 of reciprocal theorems of various kinds in geometry and other branches of mathematics. Maxwell investigated similar theorems in electricity, some of them already known. His student Donald MacAlister, the physiologist, ap-

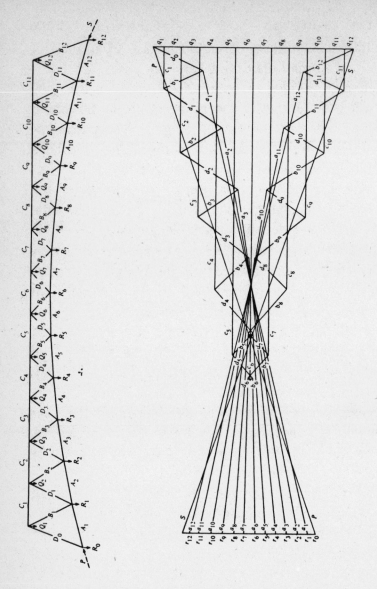

FIGURE 5.   Reciprocal diagrams for a girder bridge (1870).

plied the method to bone structures. Another application from a later period is the use of reciprocal lattices to determine atomic configurations by X-ray and electron crystallography.

In the British Association experiment on electrical resistance, Maxwell and his colleagues used a speed governor to ensure that the coil rotated uniformly. In principle it resembled James Watt's steam-engine governor: centrifugal force made weights attached to the driven shaft fly out and adjust a control valve.[94] Maxwell studied its behavior carefully; and four years later, in 1868, after reading a paper by William Siemens[95] on the practical limitations of governors, he gave an analytical treatment of the subject. He determined conditions for stability in various simple cases, including one fifth-order system representing a combination of two devices invented by Thomson and Fleeming Jenkin, and investigated effects of natural damping and of variations in the driven load, as well as the onset of instabilities. Maxwell's paper "On Governors" is generally regarded as the foundation of control theory. Norbert Wiener coined the name "cybernetics" in its honor, from $\kappa\upsilon\beta\epsilon\rho\nu\eta\tau\eta\varsigma$, the Greek for "steersman," from which, via a Latin corruption, the word "governor" is etymologically descended.[96]

Maxwell's textbook *Theory of Heat* was published

in 1870 and went through several editions with extensive revisions. Chiefly an exposition of standard results, it did contain one far-reaching innovation, the "Maxwell relations" between the thermodynamical variables, pressure, volume, entropy, and temperature, and their partial derivatives. In conceptual spirit they resemble Maxwell's field equations in electricity, by which they were obviously suggested; they are an ordered collection of relationships between fundamental quantities from which practically useful formulas follow. Several of the individual terms had previously been given by other writers. Maxwell's derivation was a deceptively simple geometrical argument based on the pressure-volume diagram. Applications of geometry to thermodynamics underwent an extraordinary development in 1873 through Gibbs's work on entropy-volume-temperature surfaces, of which Maxwell instantly became a powerful advocate. Maxwell's papers and correspondence contain much of related interest, including an independent development of the chemical potential and an admirable discussion of the classification of thermodynamic quantities in a little-known article, "On Gibbs' Thermodynamic Formulation for Coexistent Phases." In 1908 this paper was reprinted at the request of the energeticist W. Ostwald, with notes by Larmor.[97] One more important personage in the *Theory of Heat* was Maxwell's "sorting demon" (so named by Thomson), a member of a class of "very small BUT lively beings incapable of doing work but able to open and shut valves which move without friction and inertia"[98] and thereby defeat the second law of thermodynamics. The demon points to the statistical character of the law. His activities are related to the so-called "reversibility paradox" discussed first by Thomson in 1874—that is, the problem of reconciling the irreversible increase in entropy of the universe demanded by thermodynamics with the dynamical laws governing the motions of molecules, which are reversible with respect to time. A more formal view of the statistical basis of thermodynamics was supplied by Boltzmann in 1877 in the famous equation $S = k \overline{\log W}$, which relates entropy S to a quantity W expressing the molecular disorder of a system.

Maxwell's last eight years were principally devoted to Cambridge and the Cavendish Laboratory. In 1871 he had written to Rayleigh: "I hope you will be in Cambridge occasionally yourself for it will need a good deal of effort to make Exp[erimental] Physics bite into our university system which is so continuous and complete without it. . . . If we succeed too well and corrupt the minds of youth till they observe vibrations and deflexions, and become Senior Op[time]s instead of wranglers we may bring the whole university and all the parents about our ears."[99] Maxwell's charm, and the help he gave to those outside the laboratory, slowly disarmed opposition. Many papers by Cambridge mathematicians of the period acknowledge suggestions from him. Within the laboratory individual students had much more freedom to pursue their own lines of research than under his successors, and the careers of those he influenced extended far beyond physics and mathematics. Ambrose Fleming, the inventor of the diode, became an electrical engineer. W. Napier Shaw took up meteorology on Maxwell's advice and became virtually the founder of that profession in Britain. Others went further afield. J. G. Butcher, who wrote in 1876 two analytical papers on viscoelasticity that are still cited in the literature, became a successful lawyer and an "uncompromising diehard Tory"[100] member of Parliament, afterward raised to the peerage as Lord Danesfort. Donald MacAlister, the senior wrangler in 1877, an "admirable Crichton" who was also a linguist, philosopher, theologian, and physician, was for many years president of the General Medical Council and principal of Glasgow University. A letter from MacAlister to his parents in July 1877 offers a nice glimpse of Maxwell, with whom he had just dined, as "one of the best of our men, and a thorough old Scotch laird in ways and speech."[101]

The design for the Cavendish Laboratory was

176

worked out in great detail by Maxwell, along with Coutts Trotter of Trinity College and W. M. Fawcett, the architect. It embodied many ingenious features: clear corridors and stairwells for experiments needing large horizontal and vertical distances, an iron-free room for magnetic measurements, built-in antivibration tables for sensitive instruments supported by piano wires from the roof brackets, and so on. The construction of the building and much of the equipment were paid for by the Duke of Devonshire, but after 1876 Maxwell had to spend substantial sums out of his own pocket to keep the laboratory going. A characteristic of the work done under his direction was an emphasis on measurements of extreme precision, in marked contrast to the "string-and-sealing-wax" tradition of research later built up by J. J. Thomson. Examples were D. MacAlister's test of the inverse-square law in electrostatics; G. Chrystal's test of the linear form of Ohm's law; J. H. Poynting's improved version (the first of many) of Cavendish's experiment to measure the gravitational constant; and R. T. Glazebrook's determination of the optical wave surface for birefringent crystals. In each instance the precision was several orders of magnitude higher than anything previously attempted. "You see," wrote Maxwell to Joule, "that the age of heroic experiments is not yet past."[102]

NOTES
BIBLIOGRAPHY
ILLUSTRATION CREDITS
INDEX

Notes

1. See L. Campbell and W. Garnett, *The Life of James Clerk Maxwell* (London, 1882), 12, 430, 41, 67, 69, 176, 327, for this and subsequent quotations in this chapter; the letter to W. Huggins appears only in the rare second edition (London, 1884), 260.
2. C. G. Knott, *Life and Scientific Work of Peter Guthrie Tait* (Cambridge, 1911), 4, 5.
3. D. Gill, *History of the Royal Observatory, Cape of Good Hope* (London, 1913), xxx, xxxi.
4. W. C. Henry, *Life of Dalton* (London, 1854), 25–27, letter of 20 May 1833; the letter was familiar to Maxwell through G. Wilson, *Researches on Colour Blindness* (Edinburgh, 1855), 60, in which his own work was first published. See also J. Herschel, "Treatise on Light," in *Encyclopaedia Metropolitana* (London, 1843), 403.
5. W. D. Niven, ed., *The Scientific Papers of James Clerk Maxwell*, I, 146.
6. T. Young, *Lectures on Natural Philosophy*, I (London, 1807), 440; as was known to Maxwell, *Papers*, I, 150. The choice had also been suggested by C. E. Wünsch, *Versuche und Beobachtungen über die Farben des Lichtes* (Leipzig, 1792), of which an abstract is given in *Annales de chimie*, **64** (1807), 135. This rare reference is noted in one of Maxwell's memorandum books preserved at King's College, London.
7. *Papers*, I, 135.
8. J. Larmor, ed., *Memoir and Scientific Correspondence of Sir G. G. Stokes*, II (London, 1910), 22; *Life*, 376–379; W. D. Wright, *The Measurement of Colour* (London, 1944), 62 f.
9. *Life*, 347.

10. R. M. Evans, in *Journal of Photographic Science,* **9** (1961), 243; *Scientific American,* **205** (1961), 118.

11. *Papers,* I, 288. There is much of interest in the Challis-Thomson correspondence, Kelvin Papers, Cambridge University Library, file box 2.

12. *Life,* 295.

13. A. F. Cook and F. A. Franklin, in *Astronomical Journal,* **69** (1964), 173–200; **70** (1965), 704–720; **71** (1966), 10–19; also G. P. Kuiper, D. P. Cruikshank, and V. Fink, in *Bulletin of the American Astronomical Society,* **2** (1970), 235–236; and C. B. Pilcher, C. R. Chapman, L. A. Lebotsky, and H. H. Kieffer, *ibid.,* 239.

14. *Life,* 291.

15. Quoted by J. Larmor, in *Proceedings of the Royal Society,* **81** (1908), xix.

16. *Treatise,* preface, vi.

17. *Life,* 302.

18. *Proceedings of the Cambridge Philosophical Society. Mathematical and Physical Sciences,* **32** (1936), 695–750.

19. *Treatise,* I, sec. 72.

20. *Elementary Treatise,* sec. 64.

21. L. Euler, *Letters to a German Princess . . .,* H. Hunter, trans., II (London, 1795), 265–271; and known to Faraday, *Experimental Researches,* III, sec. 3263.

22. W. Thomson, *Papers on Electrostatics and Magnetism* (London, 1873), secs. 573 f., 733 f. See Maxwell's *Papers,* I, 453.

23. W. Thomson, in *Proceedings of the Royal Society,* **8** (1856), 150–158; repr. in *Baltimore Lectures* (London, 1890), app. F, 569–583.

24. J. Bromberg, Ph.D. thesis (Univ. of Wis., 1966); A. M. Bork, private communication.

25. *Proceedings of the Cambridge Philosophical Society,* **32** (1936), 704, letter of 13 Nov. 1854.

26. *Papers,* I, 500.

27. *Report of the British Association for the Advancement of Science,* 1st ser., **32** (1863), 130–163; repr. with interesting

additions in F. Jenkin, *Reports of the Committee of Electrical Standards* (London, 1873), 59–96.

28. Gauss introduced only the definition of the magnetic pole; credit for the remaining parts of the system is shared by Weber, Thomson, and Maxwell.

29. I. B. Hopley, in *Annals of Science*, **15** (1959), 91–107.

30. *Life*, 342. Letter of 5 Jan. 1865.

31. *Papers*, II, 662–663.

32. W. Thomson, *Paper on Electrostatics and Magnetism* (London, 1873), 447–448n.

33. *Report of the British Association for the Advancement of Science*, 1st ser., **32** (1863), 163–176.

34. W. Thomson, *Mathematical and Physical Papers* (Cambridge, 1882–1911), II, 61–103.

35. *Treatise*, 3rd ed., II, 228. Other illustrations were given by Boltzmann and Rayleigh. The original MS of Maxwell's 1865 paper, preserved in the archives of the Royal Society, contains a curious canceled passage likening the action of two inductive circuits on the field to the action of two horses pulling on the swingletree of a carriage. This in essence is Rayleigh's analogy.

36. Comment on a paper by G. Forbes, in *Proceedings of the Royal Society of Edinburgh*, **9** (1878), 86.

37. *Treatise*, II, sec. 575; Rayleigh (4th Baron), *Life of Lord Rayleigh* (London, 1924), 48, letter from Maxwell to Rayleigh of 18 May 1870.

38. *Papers,* I, 485n; *Treatise*, II, sec. 575.

39. A subject on which much ink has been spilled; the clearest physical treatment is by L. Page and N: I. Adams, in *American Journal of Physics*, **13** (1945), 141.

40. *Treatise*, II, sec. 615.

41. *Ibid.*, secs. 600–601.

42. G. G. Stokes, *Mathematical and Physical Papers*, IV (Cambridge, 1904), 157–202.

43. J. Larmor, ed., *Memoir and Scientific Correspondence of Sir G. G. Stokes*, II (London, 1910), 25–26. Letter to Stokes of 15 October 1864.

44. Lord Rayleigh, *Scientific Papers*, I (Cambridge, 1900), 111–134, 518–536; J. Willard Gibbs, *Scientific Papers*, II (London, 1906), 223-246; Maxwell's account, *Papers*, II, 772 f.

45. Thomson, *Mathematical and Physical Papers*, III, 466, 468.

46. *Treatise*, II, sec. 866.

47. *Life*, 394, letter to Bishop Ellicott of 22 Nov. 1876.

48. W. Whewell, *Philosophy of the Inductive Sciences*, 2 vols. (London, 1840), *passim*. See *Life*, 215, letter to R. B. Litchfield of 6 June 1855.

49. *Papers*, I, 564.

50. Thomson, *Mathematical and Physical Papers*, II, 28; for Maxwell's comments, see *Papers*, II, 767–768.

51. T. Young, in *Philosophical Transactions of the Royal Society*, **94** (1804), 1.

52. Unpublished MS at Cambridge. "On an Experiment to Determine Whether the Motion of the Earth Influences the Refraction of Light."

53. The letter is lost but see Maxwell's reply dated 6 May 1864 in J. Larmor, ed., *Memoir and Scientific Correspondence of Sir G. G. Stokes*, II (London, 1910), 23–25. I am indebted to Dr. A. M. Bork for the connection, which is obscured by the first part of Larmor's footnote on p. 23.

54. W. Huggins, in *Philosophical Transactions of the Royal Society*, **158** (1868), 532.

55. *Nature*, **21** (1880), 314, 315. See Michelson's comments in *American Journal of Science*, **122** (1881), 120; also J. C. Adams to Maxwell (17 July 1879) on the feasibility of the astronomical test (Cambridge MSS).

56. Reprinted with the FitzGerald-Lorentz correspondence in S. G. Brush, *Isis*, **58** (1967), 230–232.

57. *Treatise*, II, sec. 769.

58. *Papers*, II, 121–124.

59. Cf. J. E. McDonald, in *American Journal of Physics*, **33** (1965), 706–711.

60. *Papers*, II, 329–331, 391–392.

61. In order of citation, secs. 86, 95–102, 19–21, 280–282 with app.; and 129.

62. Secs. 756–757 and app. to ch. 17.
63. The first statement is in a letter to Thomson of 5 June 1869, in *Proceedings of the Cambridge Philosophical Society*, **32** (1936), 738–739. See J. Bromberg, in *American Journal of Physics*, **36** (1968), 142–151.
64. Thomson, *Papers on Electrostatics and Magnetism*, 15–41, paper of 1845; F. O. Mossotti, in *Archives des sciences physiques et naturelles*, **6** (1847), 193.
65. Y. Aharonov and D. Bohm, in *Physical Review*, **115** (1959), 485–491; **123** (1961), 1511–1524.
66. *Papers*, II, 43.
67. *Life*, 142–143; C. C. Gillispie, *Scientific Change*, A. C. Crombie, ed. (London, 1963), 431 ff.; S. G. Brush, *Kinetic Theory*, I (Oxford, 1965), 30n.; Elizabeth Wolfe Garber, thesis (Case Institute, 1966), and in *Historical Studies in the Physical Sciences*, **2** (1970), 299; P. M. Heimann, in *Studies in History and Philosophy of Science*, **1** (1970), 189.
68. M. Kac, in *American Journal of Mathematics*, **61** (1939), 726–728. See also T. H. Gronwall, in *Acta mathematica*, **17** (1915), 1.
69. J. Larmor, ed., *Memoir and Scientific Correspondence of Sir G. G. Stokes*, II (London, 1910), 10.
70. *Report of the British Association for the Advancement of Science*, **28**, pt. 2 (1860), 16.
71. "My better $\frac{1}{2}$, who did all the real work of the kinetic theory is at present engaged in other researches. When she is done I will let you know her answer to your enquiry [about experimental data]." Postcard from Maxwell to Tait, 29 Dec. 1877, Cambridge MSS.
72. *Life*, 80.
73. *Papers*, II, 379–380.
74. *Papers*, II, 681. Royal Society Archives 1878, Maxwell 70, Thomson's report marked 123 in upper right-hand corner. See S. G. Brush and C. W. F. Everitt, in *Historical Studies in the Physical Sciences*, **1** (1969), 105–125.
75. See S. G. Brush, in *American Journal of Physics*, **24** (1962), 274n.

76. Letter from C. Truesdell to C. W. F. Everitt, 16 Dec. 1971.
77. *Papers*, II, 376.
78. *Nature*, **20** (1877), 242.
79. *Life*, 570; A. Schuster, *The Progress of Physics 1875–1878* (Cambridge, 1911), 29; also *History of Cavendish Laboratory* (London, 1910), 31.
80. See the two eds. of Watson's *Treatise on the Kinetic Theory of Gases* (Oxford, 1876; 2nd ed., 1893); and the commentaries on Maxwell's paper by Boltzmann, in *Philosophical Magazine*, **14** (1882), 299–312; by Rayleigh, *ibid.*, **33** (1892), 356–359, and *Scientific Papers*, III, 554; and by J. Larmor, *Mathematical and Physical Papers*, II (Cambridge, 1929), app. III, 743–748. Rayleigh incorrectly attributes one of Watson's results to Maxwell, as Watson, in the 2nd ed. of his book (pp. 22–23), succeeds in pointing out, without appearing to do so, with the beautiful oblique courtesy to be expected from the man who was, after all, the Rector of Berkswell.
81. *Life*, 570–571.
82. *Papers*, II, 692.
83. *Proceedings of the Royal Society*, **27** (1878), 304.
84. *Papers*, II, 742.
85. *Treatise*, I, sec. 135a.
86. Letter of 11 July 1961 from S. C. Chapman to S. G. Brush quoted in S. G. Brush, in *American Journal of Physics*, **24** (1962), 276n.
87. E. Ikenberry and C. Truesdell, in *Journal of Rational Mechanics and Analysis*, **5** (1956), 4–128.
88. *Papers*, I, 79.
89. R. K. Luneberg, *Lectures on Optical Design* (Providence, R.I., 1944), mimeographed notes.
90. *Life*, 221.
91. For example, C. G. Wynne, in *Proceedings of the Physical Society of London*, **65B** (1952), 429.
92. W. J. M. Rankine, *Miscellaneous Scientific Papers* (London, 1881), 564.
93. *Papers*, II, 161–207; Royal Society Archives 1869.

186

94. A photograph of the governor designed by Fleeming Jenkin is given by I. B. Hopley, in *Annals of Science*, **13** (1951), 268. See also Otto Mayr, in *Isis*, **62** (1971), 425–444; and *Notes and Records. Royal Society of London*, **26** (1971), 205–228.

95. C. W. Siemens, in *Philosophical Transactions of the Royal Society*, **156** (1866), 657–670.

96. Norbert Wiener, *Cybernetics, or Control and Communication in the Animal and the Machine* (Cambridge, Mass., 1948), 11–12.

97. *Philosophical Magazine*, **16** (1908), 818.

98. C. G. Knott, *Life and Scientific Work of Peter Guthrie Tait*, 214–215.

99. Rayleigh (4th Lord), *John William Strutt, Third Baron Rayleigh* (London, 1924), 49, 50.

100. J. A. Venn, *Alumni Cantabrigiensis, Part II 1752–1900* (Cambridge, 1951) **1**, 474.

101. Edith F. B. MacAlister, *Sir Donald MacAlister of Tarbert* (London, 1935), 48.

102. *History of the Cavendish Laboratory,* 31.

Bibliography

I. ORIGINAL WORKS. Most of the technical papers were reprinted in *The Scientific Papers of J. Clerk Maxwell*, W. D. Niven, ed., 2 vols. (Cambridge, 1890; repr. New York, 1952), cited in the footnotes as *Papers*. About twenty papers and short articles were omitted from the collection; most may be found in *Nature, Electrician, Reports of the British Association, Proceedings of the London Mathematical Society, Proceedings of the Royal Society of Edinburgh*, and *Cambridge Reporter*. The abstracts of longer papers printed in the *Proceedings of the Royal Society* are also often of interest. Maxwell's books are *Theory of Heat* (London, 1870; 4th ed. greatly rev., 1875; 11th ed. rev. with notes by Lord Rayleigh, 1894); *Treatise on Electricity and Magnetism*, 2 vols. (Oxford, 1873); 2nd ed., W. D. Niven, ed. (1881); 3rd ed., J. J. Thomson, ed. (1891), cited as *Treatise*—revision of the 2nd ed. was cut short by Maxwell's death; the changes in the first eight chs. are extensive and significant; references here are to the 3rd ed.; *Matter and Motion* (London, 1877), 2nd ed., with appendixes by J. Larmor (1924); *Elementary Treatise on Electricity*, W. Garnett, ed. (Oxford, 1881; 2nd ed., rev., 1888), cited as *Elementary Treatise*; and *The Unpublished Electrical Writings of Hon. Henry Cavendish* (Cambridge, 1879), 2nd ed., with further notes by J. Larmor (1924), which contains an introductory essay and extensive notes by Maxwell.

189

II. SECONDARY LITERATURE. The standard biography is L. Campbell and W. Garnett, *The Life of James Clerk Maxwell* (London, 1882), cited as *Life;* 2nd ed., abridged but containing letters not given in 1st ed. (1884). Extensive correspondence appears in *Memoir and Scientific Correspondence of Sir George Gabriel Stokes*, J. Larmor, ed., 2 vols. (London, 1910); C. G. Knott, *Life and Scientific Work of Peter Guthrie Tait* (Cambridge, 1911); Silvanus P. Thomson, *Life of Lord Kelvin*, 2 vols. (London, 1912); J. Larmor, "The Origin of Clerk Maxwell's Electric Ideas as described in Familiar Letters to W. Thomson," in *Proceedings of the Cambridge Philosophical Society. Mathematical and Physical Sciences*, **32** (1936), 695–750, repr. as a separate vol. (Cambridge, 1937). Other letters or personal material will be found in standard biographies of W. C. and G. P. Bond, H. M. Butler, J. D. Forbes, J. G. Fraser, F. Galton, D. Gill, F. J. A. Hort, T. H. Huxley, Fleeming Jenkin, R. B. Litchfield (by Henrietta Litchfield [London, 1903], privately printed; a copy is in the library of the Working Men's College, London), C. S. Peirce, Lord Rayleigh, H. Sidgwick, W. Robertson Smith, Sir James FitzJames Stephen, and George Wilson, and in the collected papers of T. Andrews, Sir William Huggins, J. P. Joule, J. Larmor, and H. A. Rowland.

See also C. Popham Miles, *Early Death not Premature: Memoir of Francis L. Mackenzie* (Edinburgh, 1856), 216–218; W. Garnett, *Heroes of Science* (London, 1886); R. T. Glazebrook, *James Clerk Maxwell and Modern Physics* (London, 1896); F. W. Farrar, *Men I Have Known*

(London, 1897); A. Schuster, *The Progress of Physics 1875–1908* (London, 1911); *Biographical Fragments* (London, 1932); and "The Maxwell Period," in *History of the Cavendish Laboratory 1871–1910* (London, 1910), no editor identified; *Aberdeen University Quarter-Centenary Volume* (Aberdeen, 1906); D. Gill, *History of the Royal Observatory, Cape of Good Hope* (London, 1913), xxx–xxxiii, for Maxwell at Aberdeen; F. J. C. Hearnshaw, *History of King's College, London* (London, 1929); J. J. Thomson, ed., *James Clerk Maxwell 1831–1931* (Cambridge, 1931); J. G. Crowther, *British Scientists of the Nineteenth Century* (London, 1932); K. Pearson, "Old Tripos Days at Cambridge," in *Mathematical Gazette,* **20** (1936), 27; C. Domb, ed., *Clerk Maxwell and Modern Science* (London, 1963); and R. V. Jones, "James Clerk Maxwell at Aberdeen 1856–1860," in *Notes and Records. Royal Society of London,* **28** (1973), 57–81.

Useful general bibliographies are given by W. T. Scott, in *American Journal of Physics,* **31** (1963), 819–826, for the electromagnetic field concept; and by S. G. Brush in *Kinetic Theory* (Oxford, 1965, 1966, 1972) and in *American Journal of Physics,* **39** (1971), 631–640 for kinetic theory. For thermodynamics see Martin J. Klein in *American Scientist,* **58** (1970), 84–97, and Elizabeth Wolfe Garber in *Historical Studies in the Physical Sciences,* **2** (1970), 299. For the theory of governors see two articles by Otto Mayr in *Isis,* **62** (1971), 425–444; and *Notes and Records. Royal Society of London,* **26** (1971), 205–228; references to other early papers on governors are given in the later editions of E. J. Routh, *Treatise on the Dynamics of a System of Rigid Bodies,* II (6th ed., London, 1905), sec. 107.

For reciprocal diagrams see A. S. Niles, *Engineering,* **170** (1950), 194–198, and S. Timoshenko, *History of the Strength of Materials* (New York, 1953): both authors exaggerate the neglect of Maxwell's work by his contemporaries. *Studies in History and Philosophy of Science,* **1** (1970), 189–251 contains four articles on Maxwell with lengthy bibliographies. See also C. W. F. Everitt in *Applied Optics,* **6** (1967), 639–646, and P. M. Heimann in *Archives for the History of the Exact Sciences,* **6** (1970), 171–213.

The two principal collections of unpublished source materials are in the Archives of the Royal Society and in Cambridge University Library, Anderson Room, where the Stokes and Kelvin MSS should also be consulted. Materials elsewhere at Cambridge are in the Cavendish Laboratory, Peterhouse and Trinity College libraries, and the Cambridge Library. Other items are at Aberdeen University; St. Andrews University (Forbes MSS); Berlin, Staatsbibliothek der Stiftung Preussischer Kultur Besitz; Bodleian Library, Oxford (Mark Pattison MSS); Burndy Library, Norwalk, Conn.; Edinburgh University (Tait MSS); Glasgow University (Kelvin MSS); Göttingen, Niedersächsische Staats- und Universitätsbibliothek; Harvard University (Bond MSS); Imperial College, Lyon Playfair Library (Huxley MSS); Institute of Electrical Engineers (Heaviside MSS); Johns Hopkins University (Rowland MSS); Manchester Institute of Science and

Technology (Joule MSS); Queen's University, Belfast (Andrews, J. Thomson MSS); Royal Institution (Faraday, Tyndall MSS); University of Rochester, Rush Rhees Library; U.S. Air Force Cambridge Center (Rayleigh MSS).

Illustration Credits

Page 17: The Master and Fellows of Peterhouse, Cambridge

Pages 18-19, 22-23: Brigadier John Wedderburn-Maxwell

Pages 20, 28, 29, 30, 32, 33, 34 (photograph W. H. Hayles): Cavendish Laboratory

Page 21: The Master and Fellows of Trinity College, Cambridge

Page 24 (top): Cargill Gilston Knott, *The Life and Scientific Work of Peter Guthrie Tait* (Cambridge: Cambridge University Press, 1911)

Page 24 (bottom): Silvanus Thompson, *The Life of William Thomson, Baron Kelvin of Largs* (London: Macmillan, 1910); photograph by Fergus

Page 25: The Keeper of the Muniments, University of St. Andrews; photograph by G. M. Cowrie

Pages 26, 27, 31: The Syndics of Cambridge University Library

Index